SOILS
PROCESS & RESPONSE

SOILS
PROCESS & RESPONSE

I.M. FENWICK & B.J. KNAPP

DUCKWORTH

First published in 1982 by
Gerald Duckworth & Co. Ltd
The Old Piano Factory
43 Gloucester Crescent, London NW1

© 1982 I.M. Fenwick and B.J. Knapp

ISBN 0 7156 1394 4

British Library Cataloguing in Publication Data
Fenwick, I.M.
    Soils process & response.
    1. Soil science
    I. Title   II. Knapp, B.J.
    631.4   S591
    ISBN 0-7156-1394-4

Typeset by
E.B. Photosetting Ltd, Speke, Liverpool
and printed in Great Britain by
Unwin Brothers Limited,
The Gresham Press, Old Woking, Surrey

CONTENTS

Preface   vii

1.   Introduction   1

2.   Soil Mineral Matter   11

3.   The Organic Fraction   41

4.   Soil-forming Processes   59

5.   Classification and Mapping of Soils   85

6.   Soil Response   103

7.   Some Practical Exercises   165

References   193

Further Reading   205

Index   207

Colour Plates between pages 104 and 105

Acknowledgments

Thanks are due to the following people and organisations for permission to reproduce copyright material:

J. Anderson for Fig 3.3(c); J. Stout and D.S.I.R. (N.Z.) for Fig 3.3(a),(b); K. Atkinson for Figs 6.6 and 6.25 and Plate 2; P. Worsley for Plate 8; H. French for Fig 6.7; J. Hall for Fig 6.4; C. Mitchell for Fig 4.3; F.E. Broadbent and the Williams & Wilkins Co. for Table 2.2; Macaulay Institute for Soil Research, Aberdeen and the authors for Fig 6.15; Soil Survey of England and Wales for Figs 5.2, 6.20 and 6.21; W.H. Freeman and Co. & C.B. Hunt for Fig 3.1; Masson et Cie. for Fig 2.9; Oxford University Press for Figs 2.10(a), 4.11, 6.5, 6.31, Tables 5.6, 7.1; Pergamon Press for Figs 3.5 and 3.7; Elsevier Publishing Co. for Fig 4.9; N.A.S.A. for Fig 5.1; Cambridge University Press for Fig 6.28.

It has proved impossible to reach the copyright holders of Figs 6.29 and 6.30, but we are grateful to Dr A.J. Smyth, as author, for his permission to reproduce them. It has also been impossible to reach the copyright holders of Table 5.3

Preface

In recent years there has been a number of books on soils and soil geography intended primarily for geographers and other earth scientists. Why, then, another one?

Our aim has been to serve the needs of the increasing number of undergraduates in geography and other earth sciences who are taking basic courses in pedology. The subject was formerly the province of a few with specialist interest, but now a wide range of students, with varied backgrounds, are tackling what is often difficult material. Similarly many teachers are finding that their own university or college training in the subject was inadequate or even non-existent. Not surprisingly, many of them have difficulty in coping with the material on soils in 'A'-level syllabuses, some have even resorted to omitting the subject from their teaching altogether. We have had these teachers in mind when writing this book – although we do not regard it as an 'A'-level text, but rather as a source book for sixth-form teachers.

We have long felt that the coverage of soil-forming processes in the available literature is less than satisfactory. We have, therefore, directed our attention to this question. We regard the examination of processes as fundamental not only to soil geography, but also to geomorphology and to much biogeographical and ecological work.

Geographical explanation is often couched in vague and woolly terms. There is a desperate need for more rigour in both school and university teaching. We have not attempted to shield the reader from difficult concepts, but have presented topics, such as flocculation and organic matter decomposition, in a simplified way, without glossing over the true nature of the processes at work. We hope that this will help to improve the standards of geographical teaching at all levels, including our own.

A book which attempts to cover soil-forming processes and soil responses in landscapes all over the world must inevitably be largely derivative. However, it is essential to have a field familiarity with one's material, and nearly all the areas discussed in Chapter Six are ones of which we have some field experience.

It is impossible to undertake a book of this kind without the constant flow of ideas and criticism of one's colleagues. In this respect we have been particularly fortunate. We are grateful to Ray Jessop, who initiated the idea, Keith Walshaw, who has struggled to help us simplify the soil chemistry to a level comprehensible to non-chemists, Phoebe Walder, Colin Mitchell, and Peter Worsley. Ken Atkinson, Hugh French, Jo Anderson, John Stout and Colin Mitchell gave us permission to reproduce their photographs. The illustrations were drawn with painstaking care by Sheila Dance and most of the typing was done by Pamela Dixon. To Ann Fenwick must go much of the credit for this book. What at times seemed a endless task was helped along by her never-failing encouragement. Above all this book is a response to the constructive criticism of more than a decade of undergraduates who have suffered from the lectures of one of us. So strong was the criticism of one of them that he became one of the authors!

I.M.F.
B.J.K.

SYMBOLS USED IN PROFILE DIAGRAMS

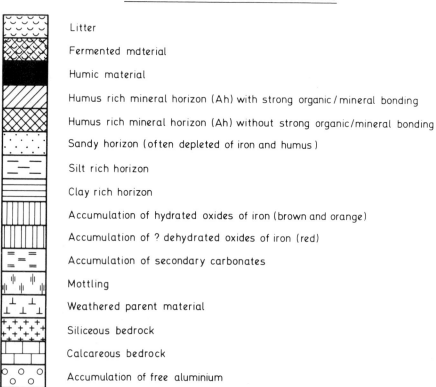

Litter

Fermented mdterial

Humic material

Humus rich mineral horizon (Ah) with strong organic / mineral bonding

Humus rich mineral horizon (Ah) without strong organic/mineral bonding

Sandy horizon (often depleted of iron and humus)

Silt rich horizon

Clay rich horizon

Accumulation of hydrated oxides of iron (brown and orange)

Accumulation of ? dehydrated oxides of iron (red)

Accumulation of secondary carbonates

Mottling

Weathered parent material

Siliceous bedrock

Calcareous bedrock

Accumulation of free aluminium

1 Introduction

Soils have been studied in different ways for thousands of years ever since the beginning of farming. At first only the topsoil was considered. Years of experience enabled the farmer to rate the potential fertility of his soil and judge the best use to which it could be put. Experience also taught him that, if he kept land in one sort of use for too long, yields would decrease.

At first farmers reacted to the exhaustion of their land by abandoning it to

Fig 1.1 Land prepared for yam cultivation after clearance by 'slash and burn'. Note the mounds on which the seedling is planted and also the use of surviving stems of saplings as poles on which the yam vine will climb

farm in a virgin location. But this was clearly wasteful, and could only be sustained where population exerted no pressure on land.

'Slash-and-burn' shifting cultivation is still practised in some parts of the tropics (*Fig 1.1*), but in general it was abandoned in western Europe before the end of the Iron Age. A settled system of agriculture brought with it the problem of maintaing the fertility and condition of the soil. The problem was solved by the use of fallow rotation, which was the basis of farming until the seventeenth century in Britain, on the mainland of Europe for even longer. The system left the soil fallow (without cultivation) for a number of years to recuperate naturally before being cultivated again.

Further pressure on land led to the replacement of this system by new rotations, in which all the land could be used all the time, given a suitable selection of crops and the use of natural fertilisers. This stage, which in Britain occurred largely in the eighteenth century, has been called the 'Agricultural Revolution'.

Agricultural practice has thus changed constantly in response to demand from an increasing population for more produce from the same amount of land. This pressure for change has never been greater than in the last hundred years. The development of scientific enquiry has coincided with a period in which land has been required to produce more and more. Many basic questions have been posed and partly answered. What properties of the soil are vital to successful agriculture? Why does the soil become exhausted? Why does it regenerate itself over time? Why are some soils more fertile than others? Why are some soils more fragile in their use than others? Why do some soils drain better than others? How can soils be upgraded to produce more?

Apart from being concerned with soil fertility, scientists turned their attention to the organisation apparent within soils. For instance, they soon realised that the properties of the upper layers, or **horizons**, to some extent reflect the nature of the sub-soil and the solid rock beneath.

As in the formative stages of any science, early soil investigators were anxious to recognise and describe the form and composition of the material they encountered. This is the approach we shall adopt in this book. One of the most obvious features of soil is its **texture**, which is determined by the proportions of discrete particles of sand, silt and clay within a sample. Here sand, silt and clay are terms used to differentiate the coarse size fraction (sand) from the finer (silt) and the finest (clay) size fractions. Texture is largely responsible for determining whether a soil is heavy (clayey) or light (sandy) – terms very familiar to the farmer.

However, further examination reveals that (except in unusual circumstances) a handful of soil does not immediately collapse into these discrete elements. Much more frequently we find that there are distinct, identifiable aggregates which have a finite strength. Only when they are crushed and rubbed between the fingers do they dismember to yield individual grains. Even then, although we cannot see this with the naked eye, it is likely that much of the clay will remain aggregated together. Aggregates are referred to as **peds** and their strength, size and shape give the soil its **structure** (see § 2.6). As we shall see in Chapter Two, texture can have an important bearing on fertility, while both texture and structure determine the properties of drainage and moisture retention. Water and air are vital for healthy plant growth, so there should be a range of pore sizes in an agricultural soil: large ones from which water will drain rapidly after a storm, and smaller ones (though not too small), in which water will be held by capillary action, and thus be available to plants. This combination of conditions is provided best by soils composed of spherical aggregates. The large voids between the peds tend to drain freely, but water is retained in the much smaller interstices within the peds, i.e. between the individual particles of sand, silt and clay.

Early pedologists, notably Dokuchaev in Russia, were perceptive enough to observe a consistent organisation in the soils they encountered. Dokuchaev was struck by the layering evident within most soils; sometimes the boundaries between these horizons are very sharp, sometimes they merge, and occasionally the boundaries show strong undulations. However, in all cases the pattern of organisation is repeated. Above the solid bedrock lies coarsely weathered, fragmented rock – the **parent material**. Frequently the parent material may not have been derived by weathering *in situ* of the bedrock but by the deposition of sediment by streams, glaciers or the action of wind. Above the parent material, and in temperate areas generally within a metre of the surface, a variety of horizons occur which have been altered considerably by internal processes. These upper horizons are grouped under the term **solum** (*Fig 1.2*).

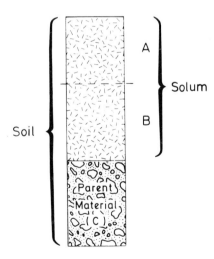

Fig 1.2   Soil and solum

The solum and the parent material together make up the soil which we can see as a **soil profile** in a pit.

There have been many attempts to define soil, but Joffe's (1949) has been widely used. He defined soil as 'a natural body of animal, mineral and organic constituents differentiated into horizons of variable depth which differ from the material below in morphology, physical make-up, chemical properties and composition, and biological characteristics'.

In the field, the profile is usually differentiated into horizons by colour. For instance, the upper horizons are often darker than the lower. While the lower part of the solum resembles in colour the parent material from which it is derived, the upper horizon often grades into the decaying leaf litter found at the surface. Furthermore, earthworms and other soil organisms are more common in the upper part of the soil and chemical investigation confirms that this horizon owes much of its colour to the presence of organic matter.

Colour contrasts may also be attributed to variations in the iron content. Of all the constituents of soil, iron compounds probably colour it most strongly – reds and browns from iron in its oxidised state, greys and blue-greens when iron compounds are reduced. When iron compounds are absent, pale greys tend to pervade the profile.

Pedologists quickly recognised that soils also showed spatial organisation,

Fig 1.3   Terracettes (short horizontal lines) and shallow slides (scars), Plynlimon, central Wales

Fig 1.4   A terminal bedrock curvature resulting from soil creep, south Pembrokeshire

that their characteristics varied with climate, with vegetation and with parent material. It is this spatial organisation and the interactive role of soils in the environment that have made pedology such a critical area of geographical investigation.

Much of the fascination and importance of the soil lies in the central role which it plays in landscape development. When the geomorphologist talks of weathering and erosion, what he is really discussing is the formation of soil and its downslope removal. Wherever there is a slope soil is always on the move; it is only the rate of erosion that varies. Erosion may be rapid, as in a landslide, or less dramatic but more pervasive, as with terracettes (*Fig 1.3*). At first sight there may seem to be no movement, but deformation of bedding planes may reveal a 'terminal curvature' (*Fig 1.4*), a tell-tale sign that the soil is moving. Ultimately, of course, this material will find its way into the streams, but it is surprising how little of the landscape is worn down directly by fluvial erosion. In the non-arid world the production and movement of soil are the main agencies of destruction.

It is clear, therefore, that slope plays a vital role in the distribution of soils – a fact which was formally suggested by Jenny (1941) when he extended Dokuchaev's original equation:

$$s = f(c,o,p)t$$

where s = soil
        c = climate
        o = organisms
        p = parent material
        t = relative age

to read:

$$s = f(c,v,o,p,r)t$$

where v = vegetation
        o = animal organisms
        r = relief

Relief influences not only soil movement but also drainage conditions. Conacher and Dalrymple (1977) have used the close relationship between pedogenic processes, geomorphic processes, soil hydrology and hillslope form as the basis for their model of landform development. To the man in the field it is probably this relationship between soils and slope form which is the most striking. This is one of the reasons why we will look at soils not as isolated phenomena, but as 'toposequences' in the landscape (Chapter Six).

There is a very close relation between soil and biosystem, and because of this some of the earlier soil classifications were essentially vegetation classifications – for example, 'soils of the coniferous forests'. At times it is difficult to establish whether plants and animals control the nature of the soil or vice versa. We will show, especially in Chapter Three, how intimate the linkage is.

At times the inter-dependence of soil, vegetation and geology may tend to mask another important relationship between soils and climate. This problem is very noticeable in Britain where climatic conditions do not vary widely, although our soils display striking contrasts. On the other hand, the early Russian pedologists, notably Dokuchaev and Sibertsev, found the correlation between the main climatic belts and the principal soil zones to be the most apparent. Today there is much interest in the variation of soil climate at a micro scale. The pattern of moisture availability has attracted particular attention: not only is it relevant to agriculture, but it also sometimes enables us to differentiate between soils by means of air photos (*Fig 5.2*). Although such patterns can be attributed to variations in moisture availability, they often reflect much greater profile contrasts, which concern the soil surveyor.

Dokuchaev also recognised that soils develop with time: 'not only are they (soils) very variable values in space, but also in certain respects comparatively unstable in time.' In this study of organisation and evolutionary change, he was, as Cruickshank (1972) puts it, 'following earlier naturalist-geographers such as Humboldt and Darwin, and geologists like Lyell and Hutton who were also preoccupied with the quality of gradual evolution'. Over time many soils have been eroded, while others have received sedimentary additions, e.g. as loess or overbank deposits.

We obviously need to examine the relationship between soils and these various environmental controls: and this is done in Chapter Six. However, we argue that this – the established approach of the Russian school – is unsatisfactory unless it is based on a firm understanding of the soil-forming processes, which we emphasise in Chapter Four. It is salutary to consider the recent history of geomorphology, in which no real progress was made for more than sixty years. Only when the critical role of process investigations was recognised was the subject able to move forward again.

Once we understand the major processes responsible for soil formation, the reasons for that evident organisation to which we have referred become clear. In some cases it is clear that upper and lower horizons have been differentiated by the movement of materials from one to the other, either in solution or in suspension. On other occasions layering may be due to sedimentary or weathering processes. Dokuchaev was quick to acknowledge the value of a shorthand notation by which to identify the main horizons and he adopted the ABC system of nomenclature: A to refer to the surface horizons and C to the parent material, the B horizon being regarded as transitional. However, largely through the work of P.E. Müller, the close genetic link between the A (as a zone of loss) and the B (as a zone of gain) horizons was established for podzolic soils. This simple model has since proved inadequate, and it has become necessary to develop a shorthand for more types of horizon. The International Society of Soil

Science (1967) advanced a scheme of horizon nomenclature which has been widely accepted, with modifications (see Table 1.1). There are 'master horizons' which are similar to those in Dokuchaev's system, but lower-case letters are used to describe the characteristics of each horizon more precisely.

Table 1.1   Horizon designations as proposed by International Society of Soil Science (1967) and Soil Survey of England and Wales [Hodgson (1974)] with minor modifications by the authors

Master horizons

L	fresh, loose, litter deposited during the previous annual cycle
F, H	organic horizons originating as litter which have decomposed so that only some (F) or none (H) of the original plant structures are visible to the naked eye
O	an upper horizon consisting of peaty material accumulating under wet conditions
A	an horizon close to the surface in which humified organic matter is intimately associated with the mineral fraction or in which there is disturbance by cultivation
E	an horizon beneath the O or A horizons, being depleted in organic matter and/or sesquioxides and/or clay
B	a mineral subsurface horizon below the A or E horizons and in which rock structure is virtually obliterated; characterised by concentrations of silicate clay, sesquioxides or organic matter or alteration of the original material to produce granular, blocky or prismatic peds
C	an horizon of unconsolidated material which does not show properties of other master horizons (it may include accumulations of the more soluble salts)
CG	an intensely gleyed horizon found chiefly in Holocene sediments which have not dried significantly since they were deposited
R	consolidated bedrock

Principal suffixes

a	ashen coloured horizon
b	horizon overlying a B which contains enough evenly distributed free iron oxide to give a dominant brownish colour
ca	accumulation of calcium carbonate (e.g. Cca)
fe	illuvial accumulation of iron in podzols (Bfe), usually accompanied by carbon enrichment and in form of brittle or cemented horizon
g	strong mottling, reflecting variations in oxidation/reduction due to periodical wetness (e.g. Bg). Weaker mottling is indicated by (g)
h	humified, well decomposed organic matter (e.g. Ah or Bh)
na	high percentage of sodium in exchange complex (e.g. Bna)
ox	residual accumulation of sesquioxides in B horizon of ferrallitic soils or oxisols (Box)
p	disturbed by ploughing (e.g. Ap)
s	a B horizon characterised by a significant enrichment in oxides of iron and aluminium
t	illuvial accumulation of clay
w	an horizon showing evidence of alteration by weathering
x	fragipan (e.g. Bx)

Transitional horizons are indicated thus: AE, EB etc

Sub-horizons

Master horizons may be subdivided to indicate observable differences thus: B_1, B_2, B_3. Where there is sufficient evidence for an implied interpretation one of the suffixes listed above may be used either with or without the numerical symbols, e.g. B_1t or Bt.

It has recently become apparent that lateral as well as vertical differentiation into horizons is of concern in pedogenesis, and the value of the profile as a fundamental unit has begun to look a little frail. The Americans, in particular [US Soil Survey Staff (1975)], have begun to adopt the **pedon** (*Fig 1.5*) as their basic unit – this permits lateral variations in horizon thickness to be taken into account. A pedon has been defined as 'the smallest volume that can be called soil. Its lateral area ranges from 1 to 10 m² and is large enough to permit study of the nature of any horizons present, for a horizon may be variable in thickness and even discontinuous' [US Soil Survey Staff (1975)]. On a larger scale, lateral changes in soil characteristics often cause a clear pattern of repeated assemblages, related to topographic form. We consider these under the heading 'Soil assocations' and in the discussion of soil catenas in Chapter Six.

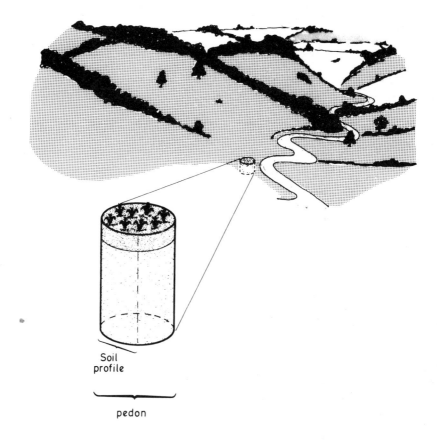

Soil
profile

pedon

Fig 1.5   The pedon as part of a landscape

Although much pedological research and soil mapping has been justified by its relevance to agriculture and, on occasions, engineering, it is in the earth sciences that the greatest benefits are often felt. The secrets of Quaternary history hidden in the soil have only just begun to be explored. Catt *et al* (1971) have demonstrated how soils often contain evidence of changing environmental conditions—of periods of aeolian sedimentation and of clay translocation, perhaps associated with changing climatic conditions.

Two themes will stand out in the following chapters—an analysis of the interactions between soils and environmental controls, and an examination of soil-forming processes. We therefore adopt an essentially geographical standpoint. We are not concerned with the applied aspects of soil study but with how and why soils develop under diverse environmental conditions.

2 Soil mineral matter

2.1 Introduction

Joffe's definition of a soil (p. 4) emphasised the observable characteristics of the profile, but a soil can also be defined in process terms as a 'heterogeneous collection of mineral and organic fragments whose disintegration has been brought about by the action of physical, chemical and biological forces working singly or in combination' [Bunting (1967)].

It follows that a particular soil results either directly from the break-up of solid rock to form the parent material or from the transport and deposition of such material from elsewhere. Subsequent processes chemically alter and stratify the upper levels of the parent material and incorporate organic matter to form the solum.

The production of the parent material and the subsequent formation of the solum is the result of many complex processes of weathering and **pedogenesis** which are discussed in this chapter and in Chapters Three and Four.

Soils play an essential part in the evolution of a landscape; they are inherent components of most erosion systems. As soil is removed from its point of formation so, in general, new soil forms to take its place. Weathering provides the parent material from which new soil develops.

2.2 Weathering

Weathering is the disintegration *in situ* of the bedrock, whether it is consolidated or not. We will consider the effect of weathering on a bare rock surface, which, with no soil or vegetative growth, is exposed to the vagaries of the weather. By day the rock is subject to heating and by night to cooling. Periodically rain falls, only to be removed by run-off, infiltration or evaporation, but not before it has had some effect on the rock surface.

The rock is a collection of minerals which are held together in various ways.

Each mineral responds differently to changes in temperature and moisture, some being more susceptible to decomposition than others. It is these less-resistant minerals which determine the rate at which the rock breaks down.

In most circumstances weathering operates primarily on the faces of rock fragments. Thus as the rock disintegrates the increasing ratio of surface area to volume is an important control on the rate of weathering (*Fig 2.1*). Strong and close jointing in rocks makes for more rapid weathering.

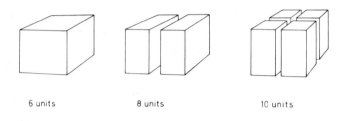

| Total Area | 6 units | 8 units | 10 units |

Fig 2.1   The effect of decreasing particle size on the surface to volume ratio

It would be wrong to assume from what has been said so far that weathering represents only a single process. Quite diverse physical and chemical changes are involved, and although many weathering processes operate in conjunction, we will consider primarily physical and primarily chemical processes separately.

2.2.1   Physical weathering

Consider a bare rock surface exposed to the elements. Moisture will be partly absorbed by the rock—the extent of absorption depending on the porosity of the rock. Some of the pores may have been created by pressure release effects. In rocks of low inherent porosity (granites and shales, for example) major joints may account for most of the voids and thus for most of the moisture. In others, for instance sandstones, pores result from the natural packing of the grains. Under such climatic regimes as are found in the sub-Arctic and

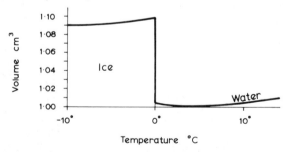

Fig 2.2   Changes in the phase and volume of water with temperature

mountainous areas the ground temperature may vary so that, either seasonally or daily, rain that has fallen and been absorbed within these pores freezes. As water freezes, so it expands (*Fig 2.2*). Since major temperature oscillations are atmospherically induced, water tends to freeze first in the joints and pores at the surface, producing a closed system. As the water within the rock begins to freeze and expand, by about 9 per cent, great pressures are exerted against the enclosing rock surfaces. These can be released by the shattering of the rock structure (*Fig 2.3*)—this is called **frost shattering**. Although it usually occurs in sub-Arctic

Fig 2.3   A rock which has been subjected to frost shattering, Morteratsch, Switzerland.

and mountainous areas, frost shattering can also be regarded as a significant process in the formation of many parent materials now found in areas of cool temperate climates. The most effective shattering in these areas is likely to have occurred during parts of the Pleistocene period when they were subject to lower temperatures than at present and to more frequent oscillations about the freezing-point.

By contrast, in areas subject to large diurnal temperature fluctuations, such as hot deserts, it is the difference in coefficients of expansion of the various minerals which is especially important. On rock surfaces diurnal temperature ranges can be well over 100 °C. Differential expansion and contraction of the constituent minerals associated with these temperature variations contributes to the stresses that cause rock fracture in deserts, when accompanied even by small amounts of moisture such as dew.

Vegetation can also play a part in physical weathering, even though its prime role is chemical. Lichens, plants which are able to attach themselves directly to rock, may swell as they take up water and thus break off tiny rock fragments (*Fig 2.4*). On a larger scale, tap roots of trees can widen fissures in rocks and eventually part blocks from the main rock mass.

Physical weathering is largely self-regulating. If material is not transported away from a site subject to physical weathering, a weathered mantle will form,

Fig 2.4   Lichens growing directly on the surface of basalt. Note that the accumulation of organic and mineral matter between the rocks has provided a suitable environment for higher plants

protecting the solid bedrock from further major temperature fluctuations. Chemical weathering, in contrast, is less subject to such limitations.

2.2.2. Chemical weathering: the primary minerals

As with physical processes, the general heading of chemical weathering covers a range of reactions – inorganic as well as organic. Inorganic processes will be considered, followed by organic changes, but the nature of the principal minerals, especially in terms of their susceptibility to decomposition, must first be studied.

Rocks can be thought of as containing:

- primary minerals, not yet affected by weathering
- in the case of sedimentary rocks, secondary minerals which have undergone at least one weathering phase

Secondary minerals occur either as clay minerals or as uncombined oxides or carbonates. Oxides and hydroxides of iron and aluminium (Fe_2O_3, $Al(OH)_3$) together with carbonates ($CaCO_3$, $MgCO_3$) often form coatings and cements in clastic sedimentary rocks and in soils.

Although rocks contain a vast range of primary minerals, a large proportion is accounted for by a very few (Table 2.1). Igneous and metamorphic rocks consist principally of varying proportions of:

- quartz
- the feldspars
- the micas
- the ferromagnesian or mafic minerals

Clastic sediments—those formed from the erosion products of an old land mass—are normally dominated by the resistant minerals, notably quartz and white mica (muscovite).

Quartz
Because of its very simple molecular structure quartz is one of the most stable minerals. The basic structural unit (the giant molecule) consists of a silicon atom covalently bonded to four oxygen atoms in a tetrahedral pattern (*Fig 2.5*). Quartz crystals are formed by three-dimensional linkages of these units through the shared oxygens. The space between the oxygen atoms is almost completely filled by the silicon atom which is therefore not readily displaced, giving quartz its almost inert qualities in many weathering environments. In crystalline form it is translucent, but may take on one of many colours.

Table 2.1   Principal primary rock-forming minerals

Silica

Quartz	SiO_2
Chalcedony (also known as chert and flint)	SiO_2

Alumino-silicates without iron and magnesium

Feldspars

Orthoclase	$KAlSi_3O_8$
Plagioclase	A gradational series of which the end members are albite, $NaAlSi_3O_8$, and anorthite, $CaAl_2Si_2O_8$
Muscovite (white mica)	$KAl_2(Al,Si_3O_{10})(OH)_2$

Alumino-silicates with iron and magnesium (ferromagnesian or mafic minerals)

Biotite (black mica)	$K(Mg,Fe)_3(Al,Si_3O_{10})(OH)_2$
Amphiboles e.g.Hornblende	Hydroxyl-bearing silicate of Ca, Al, Fe and Mg
Pyroxenes e.g. Augite	Silicate of Ca, Al, Fe and Mg
Olivine	$(MgFe)_2SiO_4$

Oxides and hydroxides

Hematite	Fe_2O_3
Goethite*	$\alpha FeO(OH)$
Lepidocrocite*	$\gamma FeO(OH)$
Amorphous ferric oxides (limonite)*†	$\alpha FeO(OH)$
Gibbsite	$Al(OH)_3$

* α, γ are different allotropes of $FeO(OH)$.

†   Although frequently referred to in the literature limonite is not now considered to be a distinct mineral.

Perspective   view   Section   Plan

● Silicon   ○ Oxygen

Fig 2.5   The silicon-oxygen tetrahedral structure

Feldspars

Feldspars belong to the wide range of framework aluminosilicates, in which (as with quartz) three-dimensional linkage is achieved through the shared oxygens. The basic tetrahedral strucutre of the quartz pattern is severely distorted by the replacement of some of the silicon by aluminium. This substitution of aluminium of oxygen state 3 for silicon of oxygen state 4 creates a net negative charge, since one of the oxygens is left with a spare linkage.* This can be satisfied by the absorption of small cations like K^+ or Ca^{2+} which fit into the interstices of the Si-Al-O framework, but this too contributes to the instability of the aluminosilicates. Feldspars are very common in igneous and metamorphic rocks but, because of their susceptibility to weathering, they are rarely found in sedimentary rocks. However, many of the secondary minerals found in sedimentary rocks are derived from them. The most common feldspars are orthoclase or potash feldspar and plagioclase feldspar which is really a gradation series containing varying proportions of sodium and calcium.

Micas

We have seen that in the feldspars silica tetrahedra ('SiO_4') are linked in three dimensions in a similar fashion to quartz. However, in the micas the silica tetrahedra are bonded in two dimensions only to form sheets. Between them is sandwiched an alumina (gibbsite) octahedral sheet (*Fig 2.6*)— the linkage being provided through the apical oxygens of the silica units. There are two basic forms: black mica (biotite) $K(Mg,Fe)_3(Al,Si_3)O_{10}(OH,F)_2$ and white mica (muscovite) $KAl_2(AlSi_3)O_{10}(OH,F)_2$.

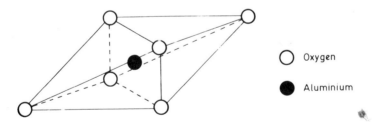

○ Oxygen

● Aluminium

Fig 2.6   The alumina octahedral structure. The linkage of such units can produce a sheet structure

Ferromagnesian (mafic) minerals

As their name implies, these are formed from a range of minerals containing a high proportion of iron and magnesium. They are grouped conventionally into three families:

* Elements are always referred to with their oxidation states, which means for a positive ion, the number of electrons lost, or, for covalently bonded atoms, the number of bonds to more electro-negative elements.

- the amphiboles (e.g. hornblende)
- the pyroxenes (e.g. augite)
- olivine

They consist of chains or bands of silica tetrahedra linked by metal cations such as iron and magnesium. The chemical composition of olivine, for example, may be written $(Mg,Fe)_2SiO_4$. They are particularly subject to weathering and rocks containing large quantities of such minerals are very prone to disintegrate. Ferromagnesian minerals are dark, with a low reflectivity, ranging in colour from green to dark brown.

2.2.3   Inorganic chemical weathering

This principally concerns the interaction of rainwater with primary rock-forming minerals. While some chemical decomposition may be due solely to the ingress of water, it must be remembered that CO_2 and SO_2, dissolved in the soil water, cause it to behave as a weak acid. Also, because the stability of minerals depends on the strength of the bonds between their constituent atoms, any change in the crystal structure is likely to lead to a change in their stability. If a cation (a positively charged ion), such as Na^+ or K^+, in the structure is replaced by one held in the enveloping solution, the replacing cation is likely to be different in size from the original. If, for example, Ca^{2+}, a relatively large ion, is the replacing cation, the structure must distort in order to accommodate it. On the other hand, if a 'hydrogen ion' replaces a metal cation a 'hole' is created because of the small size of the H ion.* Absorption of H^+ causes the structure to disintegrate [see Russell (1973) p. 699].

The principal processes involved in chemical weathering are:

- hydrolysis
- oxidation
- hydration
- solution

Hydrolysis
This is the most important process operating on primary silicate minerals. Hydrolysis reactions involve water and the mineral only, as in the case of orthoclase feldspar:

$$K_2O.Al_2O_3.6SiO_2 + 11H_2O \rightarrow Al_2O_3.2SiO_2.2H_2O + 4H_4SiO_4 + 2K^+ + 2OH^-$$

| orthoclase | water | kaolinite | silicic acid | potassium cation | hydroxyl anion |

* The hydrogen ion is hydrated and is more correctly designated H_3O^+.

Although we normally regard most minerals as unreactive in water on a short time-scale, the prolonged presence of water in a natural environment eventually results in this kind of slow reaction, which is of great practical significance.

Hydrolysis can, however, be greatly speeded up if carbon dioxide or sulphur dioxide is dissolved in the water. The presence of CO_2, for example, creates a weak carbonic acid, so that a general reaction of feldspars becomes:

aluminosilicate $+ H_2O + H_2CO_3 \rightarrow$ clay mineral $+ (Ca^{2+}, Na^+, K^+) + OH^- + HCO_3^- + H_4SiO_4$

                     carbonic   cations   bicarbonate

                     acid   anion

Reactions of this kind are often separately classed as **carbonation**. More simply, calcium carbonate (chalk, limestone) weathers to produce soluble ions alone:

$$CaCO_3 + CO_2 + H_2O \rightleftharpoons \underline{Ca^{2+} + 2HCO_3^-}$$

lime-   carbon water   soluble

stone   dioxide

The bicarbonate is very soluble but unstable and tends to be transformed into the much less soluble carbonate when there are changes in pressure, as when waters emerge from underground fissures (hence stalagmites and stalactites). When the CO_2 level falls, as in the lower regions of some soils (p. 66), the reaction moves to the left and $CaCO_3$ is precipitated.

Oxidation

Oxidation is a change of state associated with the loss of an electron. It most commonly takes place through the medium of oxygen dissolved in soil water. In soil, iron is the element most commonly oxidised. The effect is to produce brown or red colours derived from the hydrated oxides. Most iron in rock-forming minerals is in the lower valency state, Fe(II), and can sometimes be oxidised directly. More commonly iron is released by hydrolysis into an oxidising environment and, because it is unstable at most pH values, it is precipitated. Thus:

$$Fe_2SiO_4 + 2H_2CO_3 + 2H_2O \rightarrow 2Fe^{2+} + 2HCO_3^- + H_4SiO_4 + 2OH^-$$

                                     ferrous

                                     cations

which then is oxidised:

$$2Fe^{2+} + 4HCO_3^- + \tfrac{1}{2}O_2 + H_2O \rightarrow Fe_2O_3 \downarrow + 4H_2CO_3$$

                            oxygen   precipitated

                            dissolved   ferric

                            in water   oxide

In anaerobic conditions the reverse process, reduction, can lead to the production of ferrous (II) compounds.

Hydration

This is the process of adding water molecules to a mineral, giving it a new composition. It is not very important because relatively few minerals are susceptible, but one conspicuous reaction involves iron:

$$Fe_2O_3 + H_2O \rightleftharpoons 2FeO.OH$$
red   brown
hematite   goethite

Solution

Very few common minerals are directly soluble in water, i.e. dissociate into component ions. Of those that do, the chlorides of sodium and potassium are the most common. For example:

$$NaCl\ (s) \rightleftharpoons Na^+\ (aq) + Cl^-\ (aq)$$

solid   hydrated hydrated
sodium   sodium   chloride
chloride   ions   ions

This is a reversible process which depends on the salt concentration. The great importance of solution lies in its ability to remove the secondary products of other weathering processes, e.g. OH^-, HCO_3^-, K^+, Na^+.

2.2.4   Organic chemical weathering

Many of the reactions which belong under this heading are similar to those described above, but result from the interaction of organic compounds (from vegetative decomposition) and water. However, the flora and fauna within the soil also play an indirect part in weathering. For instance, the respiration of plants and animals increases the CO_2 content of the soil relative to the free atmosphere and reduces the oxygen content. As CO_2 is absorbed in the percolating water the acidity of the soil water is increased.

 The chemical effects of organic matter are inevitably concentrated in the uppermost horizon. Nevertheless, faunal activity can bring partly weathered material up to the surface where it may be more intensively altered by organic derivatives.

 Several plant and animal organisms are involved in these weathering processes and they are considered in Chapter Three, along with the reactions involving organic and mineral constituents.

2.3   The products of weathering

Clay minerals

One of the most important consequences of chemical weathering is the production of 'secondary' minerals, in particular the clay minerals, as, for instance, in the hydrolysis of orthoclase feldspar. As the clay minerals are weathering products they are inherently more stable than most of the primary minerals.

The clay minerals show certain structural similarities to the micas, as they consist of sheets of silica tetrahedra and gibbsite octahedra (*Fig 2.7*), but the kind of mineral that results depends partly on the availability of silica and of cations such as Ca^{2+}, K^+ and Mg^{2+}. The ways in which the sheets are combined are often used to differentiate between classes of clay minerals. On the basis of these criteria three common families of clays may be recognised:

- kaolinitic group
- micaceous group
- montmorillonite group

Kaolinite is the most stable of these groups. Each layer of kaolinite comprises one sheet of gibbsite and one sheet of silica (i.e. it has a 1:1 lattice structure), the sheets being bonded together through the common oxygen. Crystals between 0.2 microns and 2.0 microns may be created by the aggregation of such layers, achieved through hydrogen bonding (p. 24) between the oxygens of the silica sheet and the hydroxyls of the gibbsite sheet of the adjacent layer (*Fig 2.7*). Unsatisfied bonds (i.e. linkages) occur only at the broken edges of the sheets. The substitution of ions does not occur with this mineral and so the only forces holding cations to the clay surfaces are weak hydrogen bonds. Accordingly kaolinite displays a relatively low cation exchange capacity (see p. 24 and Table 3.2).

Hydrous micas are a more complex family of clay minerals. Formerly they were called illites but they are now known to be mineralogically mixed [Russell (1973) p. 84]. The pure micaceous clays consist of a gibbsite sheet sandwiched between two silica sheets, i.e. a 2:1 structure (*Fig 2.7*). A substantial proportion of the silicon in the silica lattice is replaced by aluminium, creating a net negative charge, a process called *isomorphous substitution* (p. 17). This is partially neutralised by potassium ions (K^+) which also link adjacent 2:1 units. These ions are so close to the source of the negative charge that the bonding is very strong and no other ions or water can enter between the main structural units.

Montmorillonites (or *smectites*) are also characterised by a gibbsite (alumina) sheet lying between two silica sheets, but in this case the negative charge is explained principally by the replacement of some of the aluminium ions in the octahedra (i.e. in the heart of the 2:1 unit) by iron and magnesium. Although the charge is neutralised by other cations they are, in this case, far removed from the seat of the charge. The linkage between adjacent units is therefore

relatively weak, so that both cations and water molecules can enter. It is this
ability to absorb water and thus force the units apart which gives
montmorillonites one of their most striking properties—that of swelling and
shrinking.

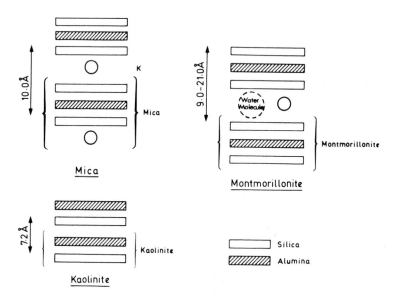

Fig 2.7   The structure of the more common soil clay minerals. The circles represent cations

In the temperate regions of the world clay minerals are normally a direct
residual product of hydrolysis. However, it is increasingly clear that in many
areas, especially the tropics, they may also result from the synthesis of silica and
alumina—themselves usually the products of hydrolysis [Weaver and Pollard
(1973)]. The type of clay which is produced depends on a variety of
environmental factors, particularly the state of drainage, the cations present in
the soil and the soil acidity. Drainage conditions are especially important here
since free drainage will encourage the elimination of soluble or fine colloidal
material from the profile. On the other hand, the retention of the alumina, silica
and bases, and therefore the formation of secondary clay, will be stimulated
where water movement is impeded.

   The precise nature of the synthesised clays is closely dependent on the
prevailing acidity (§7.2.2, p. 173). At c.pH 5–6 1:1 clays of the kaolinite group
which are low in silica tend to be formed. In neutral or alkaline media with a
concentration of Ca^{2+} or Mg^{2+} in the soil solution, provided sufficient silicic
acid is available, the dominant formation is of 2:1 minerals such as
montmorillonite.

Hydrated oxides

Weathering of the primary minerals leads to the formation of clay minerals and subsequently, under conditions of intense leaching, to the liberation of aluminium hydroxides of varying degrees of hydration, such as gibbsite ($Al(OH)_3$ or $Al_2O_3.3H_2O$):

$$Al_2Si_2O_5(OH)_4 + H_2O \rightleftharpoons Al_2O_3.3H_2O + 2SiO_2$$
kaolinite   gibbsite   silica

[after Loughnan (1969)]

Furthermore, we have already seen (p. 19) that where iron-rich minerals are present, weathering will release hydrated ferric oxides which are themselves of clay size. The mineral which is formed is largely dependent on the microclimate of the area. Thus in cool, damp locations limonite, an amorphous ochreous coloured compound, forms. Goethite ($FeO(OH)$) is reddish-brown and gives the typical brownish hues to many soils, especially in temperate lands. In the tropics, hematite (Fe_2O_3) with its characteristic rich red colour is thought to be largely responsible for the brilliant tones of the soils (Plate 1). These oxides and hydroxides of aluminium and iron (often loosely referred to as *sesquioxides*) tend to occur as cements and coatings on individual grains, particularly in the clay minerals (see § 7.3.7).

Weathering is therefore responsible for producing whole new categories of minerals whose properties differ markedly from their primary counterparts. In particular, the smaller, colloidal minerals carry an electrostatic charge, which is important in the structural stability of soils as well as their fertility. The clay minerals carry a strong negative charge (as do the organic colloids), while the sesquioxides carry a positive charge, at least in acid soils.

Table 2.2   Cation Exchange Capacity of organic and clay fractions of some new York soils

		C.E.C. (m.e./100g oven-dry soil)		
Series	**Organic matter content (%)**	**Clay**	**Organic matter**	**% due to organic matter**
Dunkirk	9.75	7.4	18.8	72
Honeoye	6.57	3.2	13.3	81
Ontario	7.34	2.7	13.7	84
Yates	5.70	3.4	9.4	73

[from Broadbent, F.E. (1955)]

Since the net charge of the clay mineral particles is negative, they attract cations and water molecules in the soil solution. Each particle carries a definite charge which will be satisfied by a specific number of cations. For example, the mean surface density of charge for clay minerals is 1.4 electrons per millimicron squared [Fripiat (1965)]. The total potential of a soil for absorbing cations is called the Cation Exchange Capacity (C.E.C.). Examples for different soils are given in Table 2.2.

2.4   The role of soil water

Water and air occupy the spaces (pores) left when irregularly shaped particles are packed together. The mineral and organic content is more or less fixed for a particular soil and usually amounts to about 50 per cent of the total bulk. The remaining 50 per cent is composed of a varying amount of air and water. Both air and water are needed for plant growth, but it is mainly the water held within the pores which causes weathering and transports soluble products away from the site.

Water is held in the soil in a variety of ways. Closest to the soil particles is a monomolecular layer of water adsorbed on the mineral surface and unavailable to plants. This adsorption results from the special nature of water molecules, which consist of two hydrogen atoms held by covalent bonding to a much larger oxygen atom. The bonding occurs in such a way that the hydrogen atoms are not positioned linearly with respect to the oxygen, but produce a V-shaped configuration $H{\diagup}^O{\diagdown}H$. In this disposition the shared electrons are closer to the oxygen than to the hydrogen, creating a slight positive charge at the hydrogen end of the molecule and a slight negative charge at the oxygen end. Each water molecule thus has a polarity which enables it to couple with neighbouring molecules and with charged mineral particle surfaces. Cations (p. 18) become hydrated through their attraction to the negative (oxygen) end of the water molecule, whilst anions and clay mineral surfaces attract water through the positive (hydrogen) end.

This weak electrostatic force caused by the asymmetry of the hydrogen atoms in the water molecule is called **hydrogen bonding**. It is very important because it enables clay minerals to hold on their surfaces not only water molecules but also hydrated cations (*Fig 2.8*). Hydrogen bonding is also important in giving kaolinite its structural rigidity; in this instance the exposed hydroxyls of the gibbsite sheet and the oxygen atoms of the adjacent silica sheet are linked through hydrogen bonds.

Soil water is also held by surface tension forces, which account for most of the water retained in a soil. Surface tension is caused by the greater attraction of water molecules for each other than for the air. Because surface tension has a finite maximum value it is only effective in small (capillary) pores where it can hold water against gravity even after a prolonged period of drainage has occurred. Thus, while some water is rigidly adsorbed to soil particle surfaces, the remainder is much more loosely held by surface tension.

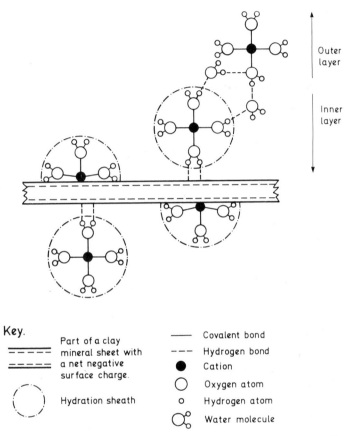

Key.

----- (dashed)	Part of a clay mineral sheet with a net negative surface charge.	——	Covalent bond
		---	Hydrogen bond
		●	Cation
(circle)	Hydration sheath	○	Oxygen atom
		o	Hydrogen atom
		♂	Water molecule

Fig 2.8   Diagrammatic representation of the possible relationship between water, cations and exchange sites on the surface of a clay mineral. Cations can be held against the mineral surface in response to a charge created by isomorphous substitution. They can be held less strongly within their hydration shell by hydrogen bonding

Away from the particle surfaces there is a gradual increase in the mobility of the water which has important effects on soil formation. For example, the interrelation between negatively charged colloids and their surrounding cations and water molecules can be regarded as a diffuse electrical double layer. The inner layer consists of the surface of the colloid carrying its negative charges and mantled by a monomolecular layer of water and cations. Surrounding this is an outer layer consisting of more loosely bonded water molecules and cations which may be interchanged with the inner layer. Once detached from the clay surface, cations are able to move into the soil solution and hence into the moving soil water. On the other hand, cations present in the soil solution may be adsorbed on to the colloid.

A whole range of cations are adsorbed on to clays and organic colloids. Some are held more strongly than others, depending on their charge to radius ratio:

Al^{3+}, Ca^{2+}, Mg^{2+}, H^+, K^+, NH_4^+, Na^+ (in increasing ease of displacement)

Al^{3+} and other polyvalent ions are most tightly bonded and the others progressively less so. H^+ is an exception: because of its small size, it behaves in many respects as a di-or a tri-valent ion. When the colloid is dominated by H^+ or Al^{3+} it is acid and the soil solution displays a low pH. On the other hand, if Ca^{2+} dominates, the soil takes on a basic reaction.

Experiment has shown that the nature of the adsorbed cation depends on the solution concentration. In a dilute solution divalent cations tend to be adsorbed and there is a relative desorption of monovalent ones [Russell (1973) p. 90]. Thus in the dilute conditions found with most percolating rainwaters, Ca^{2+} might be expected to be one of the most common adsorbed cations. In relatively concentrated solutions the reverse is true, with the colloid approaching saturation with monovalent cations such as Na^+. In dilute solutions with a low cation concentration the dissociation of water into H^+ and OH^- ions leads to most sites being occupied by H^+ (see the discussion of podzolisation in § 4.3.4).

Clearly the balance between the metal cations and H^+ is delicate, responding to changes in environmental conditions. Generally speaking, it is this balance which determines the acidity of the soil solution. In order to appreciate this we must consider the equilibrium which exists between the charged particle and the solution [Schuffelen (1974)].

Soils saturated with H^+ will equilibriate with the H^+ in solution, producing a high level of acidity. However, hydrogen is not the only ion to create acidity; Al^{3+} accounts for the acidity of many soils because of its ready hydrolysis which may be shown as:

$$Al^{3+} + 3H_2O \rightleftharpoons Al(OH)_3\downarrow + 3H^+$$

It can be seen that hydrogen ions are released into the soil solution while the collodial aluminium hydroxide may rapidly crystallise to give gibbsite (§ 4.3.7).

Most metallic cations will produce the opposite effect, since they liberate OH^-, the essence of alkalinity, into the solution:

$$K\boxed{\begin{matrix}Soil\\colloid\end{matrix}} + H_2O \rightleftharpoons H\boxed{\begin{matrix}Soil\\colloid\end{matrix}} + K^+ + OH^-$$

Adsorbed
potassium

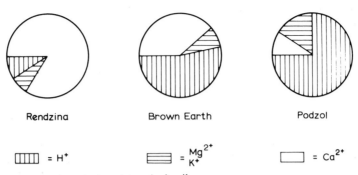

Fig 2.9   Proportions of various cations in typical soils

The balance between the metal cations and H^+ and Al^{3+} is important not only in determining the soil acidity but also in relation to fertility and pedogenesis. Potassium, in particular, is essential if other plant nutrients, such as nitrogen, are to be used efficiently. If the litter returned to the soil is deficient in certain of these cations, soil formation will be affected. Also, as we shall see in § 2.7, exchangeable cations play a central role in flocculating clays and, therefore, in developing soil structure (*Fig 2.15*).

2.5   Texture

It will be appreciated that the weathering processes discussed above result in the comminution of the parent rock until, eventually, the soil particles are virtually all of microscopic size (i.e. less than 2 μm, or 0.002 mm diameter). However, for such a state to be achieved, physical and chemical attack must proceed over a long period. We therefore find that soils contain a range of particle sizes from large boulders to fine clay. The proportions of these discrete (i.e. non-aggregated) particles in a given soil are referred to as the **soil texture**. Particle sizes vary continuously over the range, so it is necessary, for convenience, to refer to a limited number of particle-size classes. Three systems are in common use (Table 2.3):

- the 'International Classification'
- the system devised by the United States Department of Agriculture
- the system used by the Soil Survey of England and Wales

The International Classification displays a certain mathematical elegance, being a logarithmic scale. However, the USDA and British boundary between silt and fine sand has considerable practical value (see p. 31). In all the systems there is a certain rationale in that each size group is dominated by a particular mineral fraction. Coarse sand usually contains fragments of the parent material which have been physically weathered. These rock fragments comprise primary, often easily weathered, minerals such as feldspars and ferromagnesian silicates (e.g. hornblendes and augite). Fine sand and silt represent a further stage of comminution by physical and chemical means. These fractions, therefore, are normally of individual minerals, especially the more resistant primary minerals such as quartz. Clay minerals—the products of weathering of the primary feldspars, micas and ferromagnesian minerals—account for most of the clay size fraction.

Table 2.3   Particle size classes (expressed in terms of effective particle diameter)

	British system	International system	US Department of Agriculture system
Gravel	>2.0 mm	>2.0 mm	>2.0 mm
Coarse sand	2.0–0.06 mm	2.0–0.2 mm	2.0–0.2 mm
Fine sand		0.2–0.02 mm	0.2–0.05 mm
Silt	60—2 μm	20—2 μm	50—2 μm
Clay	<2μm	<2μm	<2μm

A clear distinction should be made between the term **clay**, as used to indicate a size fraction, and **clay mineral**, a term which has a purely mineralogical connotation. Indeed, the clay fraction contains not only clay minerals but also, as we have seen, other secondary products such as the hydrated oxides of iron and aluminium. Nearly all material of clay size behaves as a colloid—that is, although it is itself solid, it remains in a dispersed state when put into suspension in water. Often quoted examples of other colloids are milk, in which solid particles are dispersed throughout a liquid, and cloud, in which minute liquid droplets are suspended in a gas. However, colloids can be affected by variations in the suspending medium—in this case, the soil solution—and this has important implications, especially for soil structure (see § 2.7).

Conventionally, the textural description relates only to the fine earth fraction, i.e. less than 2.0 mm effective diameter. For a given sample it is most effective to locate the proportions of the sand, silt and clay fractions on a triangular plot (*Fig 2.10*), and for this purpose, the coarse and fine sand sizes are amalgamated. It will be seen from the diagram that soils dominated by either sand, silt or clay fall near to one of the apices of the triangle, while soils containing approximately equal proportions of these three fractions occur in a central position. It is possible thus to see at a glance the textural composition of any specimen. *Fig 2.10* and Table 2.4 show that soils developed on different parent materials often display very distinctive textural characteristics—a reflection of the extent to which weathering and sorting have been able to progress. For instance, soils developed on clastic sediments in which the grains are of resistant minerals, such as quartz, frequently take up the textural characteristics of the sediments. The Bridgnorth Series—an acid brown earth (sol brun acide, Ochrept) (§ 6.3) occurring extensively on the Bunter sandstone (Triassic) of the English Midland plain—is dominated by the sand fraction. In the analysis quoted, with 83 per cent sand in the A horizon, it falls within the loamy sand category. Similarly, in the Melton Mowbray district of Leicestershire (UK), weathering of the Liassic shales has produced a heavy clay soil, represented by the Evesham series (a gleyed calcareous soil) (§ 6.3).

However, the effects of the underlying solid rock are often modified by the deposition of transported material. Over much of northern North America and north-west Europe the Pleistocene glaciations have left behind extensive till sheets. The material comprising these deposits is the result of considerable grinding followed by chemical weathering. Soils derived from such tills, therefore, display a wide range of particle sizes, but with a notable frequency of silt and clay. The analysis from the Ardill Association of Saskatchewan—a soil developed on till of Wisconsin (the last glacial) age—displays these characteristics well.

Additions of aeolian material may also greatly alter the mechanical composition of the soil. Wind-blown deposits are normally confined to a small size range—between *c.*20 μm and 60 μm—so the mechanical analysis may well betray the presence of such material. We see that in the Poperinge soil, with a strong aeolian addition, the silt fraction is predominant. This is one of the reasons why the Soil Survey of England and Wales has adopted 60 μm as the

Table 2.4   Mechanical composition of surface horizons of soils developed on different parent materials

Location	Parent material	Mapping unit & profile ref.	% Sand 2.0—0.05 mm	% Silt 50—2 μm	% Clay <2 μm	Texture (USDA)
1. Derby, UK	Bunter sandstone	Bridgnorth Series NK 23	83	7	10	Loamy sand
2. Melton Mowbray, UK	Lias shales	Evesham Series SK62/8388	12	27	60	Clay
3. Willow Bunch Lake, Sask.	Till from Cretaceous shales	Ardill Assn	31	35	34	Clay loam
4. Poperinge, Belgium	Loess	Lbc. 81W/1	31	64	5	Silt loam

[sources: 1. Bridges, E.M. (1966); 2. Thomasson, A.J. (1971); 3. Ellis, J.G., D.F. Acton and H.C. Moss (1967); 4. Hubert, P. (1961)]

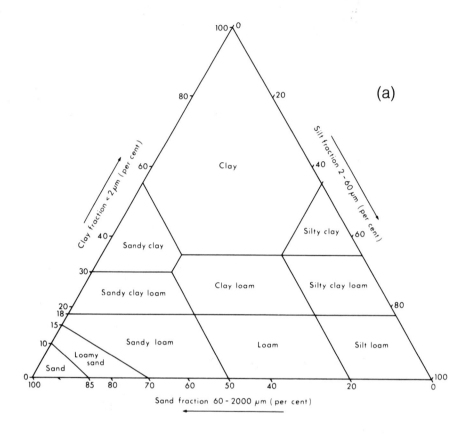

Fig 2.10   Triangular diagrams for determination of soil texture based on the limits laid down by
(a) Soil Survey of England and Wales (b) US Department of Agriculture

boundary between fine silt and fine sand and accordingly a modified triangular
plot is now used (*Fig 2.10a*). Various techniques are used to determine the
mechanical composition of a soil (see § 7.3.5).

2.6   Structure classification

Although texture influences many important aspects of soil behaviour, such as
water retention, equally significant attributes, such as the ease of drainage, are
largely determined by the manner in which the discrete particles of sand, silt
and clay **aggregate** or bond together. Such aggregates are often referred to as
peds and their shape, size and disposition define the soil structure.

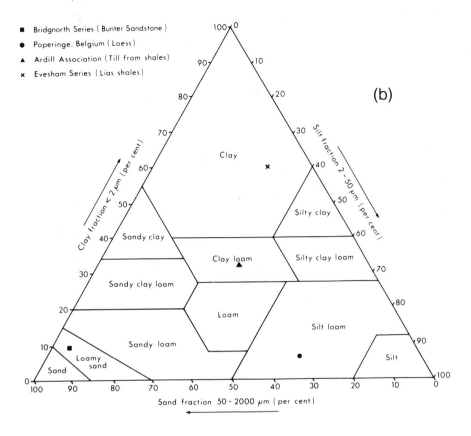

■ Bridgnorth Series (Bunter Sandstone)
● Poperinge, Belgium (Loess)
▲ Ardill Association (Till from shales)
✕ Evesham Series (Lias shales)

(b)

Clay fraction < 2 µm (per cent)

Silt fraction 2 - 50 µm (per cent)

Clay

Silty clay

Sandy clay

Clay loam

Silty clay loam

Sandy clay loam

Loam

Sandy loam

Silt loam

Loamy sand

Sand

Silt

Sand fraction 50 - 2000 µm (per cent)

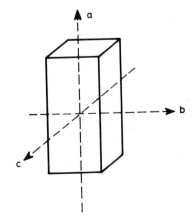

Fig 2.11   The axes referred to in the
classification of soil structures

Peds usually fall into one of a relatively small number of distinct morphological forms. When defining and recognising peds it is best to concentrate on just two characteristics—the lengths of the axes (*Fig 2.11*), and the degree of **accommodation**. Accommodation refers to the extent to which faces of adjacent aggregates are moulds one of another. Where adjacent faces meet and leave virtually no void (such as in the regular packing of cuboids) there is said to be good accommodation (*Fig 2.12a*). On the other hand, a packing of spheres displays no accommodation (*Fig 2.12b*).

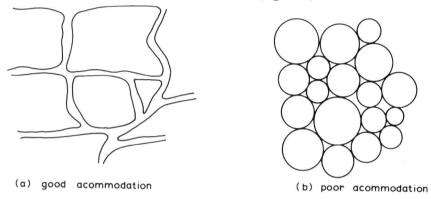

(a) good acommodation   (b) poor acommodation

Fig 2.12   Differing forms of accommodation of structural units

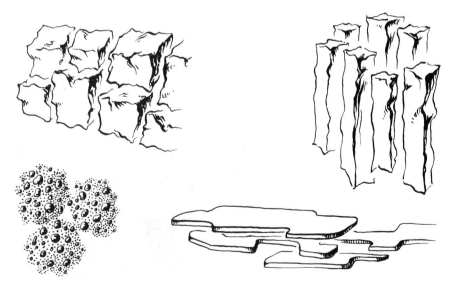

Fig 2.13   Some characteristic ped shapes:
top left: blocky   *top right*: prismatic
bottom left: spheroidal   *bottom right*: platy

Fig 2.14   The cause of drainage impedance is seen in the lower horizons of this laminar structure soil, Fraisthorpe, East Yorkshire

Two principal structural types of soil may be recognised [Clarke (1971)]: simple and compound (Table 2.5). The former displays either no bonding between the grains as, for instance, in a blown sand (**single-grained structure**), or no cleavage between the grains, as is the case in certain dispersed heavy clay soils (**massive structure**). Where compound peds (*Fig 2.13*) have formed they conventionally belong to one of four major categories:

- spheroidal: resembling roughly defined spheres, i.e. showing very little accommodation but with large interpedal pores. Peds such as this are common in the Ah horizon of grassland soils
- blocky: in which all axes are approximately the same length, resembling a cube or pyramid, but with accommodation of a high order; in gleyed soils the aggregates are frequently of this form
- prismatic: in this case the vertical (a) axis is dominant, giving a columnar form, but again displaying strong accommodation. Columnar aggregates are best displayed in saline soils where the heads of the columns are characteristically rounded. However, Bt horizons of brown earths often consist of more angular prisms
- laminar or platy: showing a dominantly horizontal disposition; in soils formed of such peds drainage is often a problem because of the suppression of vertical voids (*Fig 2.14*)

Table 2.5   Forms of soil structure

Major Group	Sub-group	Characteristics
Simple	Single grained	No bonding between grains
	Massive	No cleavage between grains
Compound	Spheroidal (granular or crumb)	a, b, c axes of approximately equal length; no accommodation
	Blocky	a, b, c axes of approximately equal length; good accommodation
	Prismatic	a axis dominant; good accommodation between adjacent peds
	Laminar (platy)	b and c axes dominant; good accommodation between adjacent peds

[source: Clarke (1971)]

2.7   Structure-forming and stabilising processes

Although it has proved relatively simple to provide an acceptable classification of structure, there is still much to be learned about the nature of the bonding forces. Russell (1971) has made this very clear, but has indicated the most likely causes of aggregation. When considering the reasons for the existence of peds one must recognise two distinct processes:

- creation
- stabilisation

The level of biotic activity is of primary importance in the formation of aggregates, especially in the upper horizons. Even the casual observer can see that plant roots and animals, such as earthworms, create voids in the soil mass and, in so doing, define structural units, normally of a spheroidal form. This is well understood by farmers who include temporary grassland and leys in their rotations.

Fragmentation of a larger soil mass is also caused by the expansion and contraction of the clay minerals (§ 2.3). As the soil dries out, either directly by evaporation or by the uptake of water through root hairs, many clays contract and create voids. Roots can penetrate into these voids and in one season alone an extensive network which helps to define the structures may be formed. Many of the prismatic and blocky aggregates found in B horizons seem to be due to such fragmentation. Finally, many soils display structural characteristics which have been inherited from the parent material. For instance, lacustrine sediments and shales are usually strongly bedded, an attribute which is often retained for some time by the lower horizons of the soils developed upon them (*Fig 2.14*).

It is these sources that we must investigate to understand the origin of the various structural forms, but their stability and strength depend to some extent on other controls.

Examination of a sandy soil immediately reveals a fundamentally unstable structure. Only when clay is present is there any strength and stability in the peds, as clay is the only mineral fraction which is able to bond together without external assistance. It has already been seen that metallic cations are adsorbed on the surface of clay and organic colloids. We must now examine the effects which different cations have on the behaviour of their host colloids.

Flocculation

If we consider a clay in suspension in water, it is clear that the negatively charged colloids will repel each other and, therefore, remain dispersed. But if these charges are nullified by cations such as Na^+ or Ca^{2+}, particles may collide and adhere to each other to form microaggregates. This is called flocculation.

However, there are more positive reasons for flocculation. When colloids approach one another closely enough, forces of molecular attraction (van der Waals' forces) become effective and cause adhesion. Clays rarely carry only negative charges, and under acid conditions parts of their surface are positively charged, particularly the so-called broken edges. This provides a possible way to link adjacent clay colloids (shown schematically in *Fig 2.15a*)—the positive charges on the broken edges being attracted to the negative charges on the adjacent clay surface (or even organic unit). In this way edge-to-face orientation may be produced. However, such a linkage can be disrupted if the cations in the soil solution are able to blanket the positive charges on the broken edges. Cations which are held closely to the clay surface, particularly the divalents and trivalents, will not be able to accomplish this (*Fig 2.15b*), and aggregation will be possible. However, monovalent cations, particularly Na^+, are held very loosely so that although they are in a very diffuse double layer relating to the faces of the clays they may effectively blanket any positive charges on the broken edges (*Figs 2.15c*), and the flocs will disperse.

Finally, polyvalent cations can link both organic and mineral colloids extremely effectively by acting as bridges between them (*Fig 2.15d*). Ca^{2+} saturated montmorillonites are perhaps the best example of this face-to-face bonding. Bridging is again inhibited by a thick double layer such as is produced by Na^+ domination (*Fig 2.15e*).

Not all colloids carry negative charges. In acid conditions the hydrated oxides of both iron and aluminium are positively charged and thus act in much the same way as metallic cations. That flocculation can be encouraged by these oxides, especially aluminium hydroxide, is of particular significance in acid environments where the 'flocculating divalents' have largely been replaced on the exchange complex.

While flocculation may be a potent force linking individual colloidal particles it is generally agreed that only micro-aggregates or **domains** of perhaps less than 100 μm diameter are likely to result. Casual examination of a handful of soil immediately reveals larger aggregates containing not only clay but also sand and silt. We must, therefore, look for other cementing agents.

Cementing agents

Three groups of constitutents have been isolated which are capable of playing this role: colloidal ferric and aluminium oxides, calcium carbonate and organic material.

Ferric oxide mantles mineral grains of all sizes. In the case of sand grains this can readily be seen by comparing two samples, one treated with sodium dithionite, $Na_2S_2O_4$, and the other untreated (see § 7.3.7 for experimental details). Only where the soil has been heavily leached (§ 4.3.4) will the two specimens appear similar. Normally, the untreated material is brown and opaque, while 'cleaning' exposes numerous quartz grains which are translucent. If processes involving the mobilisation and redeposition of sesquioxides are active, the coarser sand and silt fractions may be veiled where precipitation is taking place. Eventually bridges may form between separate particles and domains of flocculated clay (*Fig 2.16*).

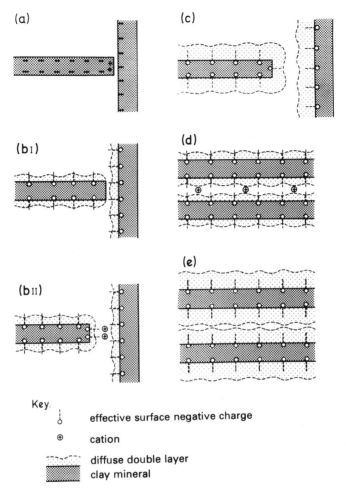

Key.

effective surface negative charge

⊕   cation

diffuse double layer

clay mineral

Fig 2.15   The basic concept of edge-to-face attraction of clay mineral platelets is outlined in (a). However, all platelets are blanketed, at least in part, by the diffuse double layer. In acid soils with a thin compressed double layer, produced by Al^{3+} saturation, the positively charged broken edges can attract the negative surface charge produced by surface oxygens that have not been satisfied by cations within the double layer (bI). In soils with a basic reaction, but also with a thin compressed double layer such as is produced by Ca^{2+} domination, the broken edges are negative but flocculation can still take place through the intermediary of hydrated cations within the soil solution (bII). However, with a thick, expanded double layer, such as occurs with Na^+ domination, the negative charge effect caused by surface oxygen does not penetrate right through the double layer and flocculation is inhibited (c). The same effects are seen between platelet surfaces for cations with a high charge to radius ratio (d), giving a compressed layer and flocculation; and for cations with a low ratio and expanded double layer preventing flocculation (e)

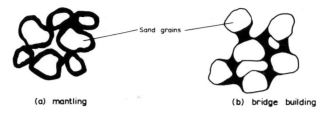

(a) mantling   (b) bridge building

Fig 2.16   The role of hydrated oxides in structure formation

Calcium carbonate: a similar function is performed by the secondary accumulation of calcium carbonate, $CaCO_3$, in calcareous soils.

Organic material: when discussing the strength and stability of aggregates most emphasis must be placed on the role of organic matter [Duchaufour (1976)]. Soil humus contains polysaccharide gums which are polymers of a range of sugars. These are generally very large molecules with molecular weights of more than 100 000 and sometimes even greater than 1 million. Soil micro-organisms, especially those responsible for the breakdown of decaying roots, appear to be the prime producers of the gums which link the fractions together. Although the position is not yet fully understood, it seems likely that it is the polysaccharides which are most effective in holding soil particles together in a loose but strong structure of chain-like molecules which form nets around the mineral particles. However, other organic constituents are almost certainly involved. Organic molecule and clay are linked in various ways, notably by the direct adsorption of organic cations on to the clay surface and, where large organic cations are involved, by van der Waals' forces which bind them to the clays [Mortland (1970)]. Edwards and Bremner (1967) have shown that organic molecule and clay can be linked through hydrogen bonding via the water molecule which forms part of the hydration shell of the exchangeable cation (*Fig 2.8*).

Summary
Peds must be created and then maintained as stable entities. They may be formed by constructive processes due to:
- the availability of an adequate supply of polyvalent cations causing flocculation
- biotic activity, notably earthworms, forming casts

or by fragmentation caused by:
- shrinking and swelling of the clay minerals to produce angular peds
- the burrowing action of various animals and the development of root systems

The origin of structural units varies with depth. In the upper horizons the structure is created mainly by the penetration of root systems and the burrowing of small animals. Lower down the profile, units are largely a response to expansion and contraction of the clays.

Peds are maintained as stable structures by:
- the cementing effect of the oxides of iron and aluminium and of secondary precipitates of calcium carbonate
- the bonding achieved by polyvalent cations
- the binding effect of polysaccharide gums, generated by micro-organisms

Soil structural units are preserved by:
- continued biochemical breakdown of organic matter to replenish the polysaccharides and other organic gums which gradually oxidise
- high levels of polyvalent cations produced by continued weathering of minerals *in situ* and decomposition of fresh organic matter
- the continued availability of iron oxide cements

Texture and structure are very important in both pedogenesis and agriculture. The processes of soil formation are examined in Chapter Four, and it will become evident that the translocation of material through the profile can only take place once the aggregate-bonding agents have been at least partially destroyed. Moreover drainage conditions, which are very significant in soil formation, are closely related to the strength and stability of the structure. While porous spheroidal peds retain ample moisture for plant growth they also allow the free passage of surplus water via the interpedal voids. In such conditions root systems prosper. Slaking of the ped walls, however, clogs the pores with clay and prevents the free circulation of water and air.

3 The organic fraction

3.1 Soil organic matter: form and function

Soil organic matter is an umbrella term for the entire range of organic tissue present within the soil. From whatever source such material originates it comprises, besides water, three principal components:

- carbohydrates: celluloses (fibres of which form plant cell walls) and hemicelluloses (which encrust cellulose fibres), sugars and starches and lignin (a component highly resistant to decomposition and helping to form woody tissue)
- protein: important as it is the main stock of organic nitrogen
- waxes, fats and resins

Table 3.1 demonstrates very clearly the varying composition of different types of plants and different parts of plants.

The components of soil organic matter decay at quite different rates and fulfil quite different roles. It is generally true to say that, of the organic materials, the celluloses decompose most readily, while lignin is the most resistant. Thus fully grown plants, especially woody plants which contain a high proportion of lignin, decompose slowly. Decay is accomplished mainly by micro-organisms whose form and function are considered in § 3.3.

During the process of decomposition and associated microbial metabolism new organic compounds are produced, resulting in an increase in the soil of, amongst others, proteins, polysaccharides and humic acids. Many of the insoluble end-products are extremely small and display colloidal properties. In colloidal form organic matter is able to adsorb many more cations per unit of surface area than even the clay minerals; that is, it possesses a higher cation exchange capacity (Table 3.2).

When organic debris decomposes it produces, *inter alia*, acidic compounds. These operate in much the same way as inorganic acids, such as carbonic acid

Table 3.1   Approximate chemical composition of higher and lower plant organisms (as % of dry matter)

Organisms investigated	Waxes fats resins	Protein	Cellulose	Hemicellulose & soluble carbohydrates	Lignin
Perennial leguminous plants					
Roots	10–12	10–15	20–25	25–30	10–15
Leaves	–	12–20	15	10–12	5
Perennial grasses					
Roots	5–12	5–10	25–30	25–30	15–20
Deciduous species					
Leaves	3–5	4–10	15–25	10–20	10
Wood	–	0.5–1	40–50	20–30	20–25
Coniferous species					
Needles	20–25	5–7	20	15–20	15
Wood	–	0.1–1	45–50	15–25	25–30

[source: Kononova (1966) p. 112]

Table 3.2   Comparison of cation exchange capacities

	Cation exchange capacity at pH 7 (m.e./100 g oven dry soil)
Kaolinite	3–15
Hydrous micas (illite)	10–40
Montmorillonite	80–150
Humus	150–500

[source: Grim (1968) pp. 189, 193]

(H_2CO_3), and are therefore important weathering agents. When deeply penetrating root systems begin to decay, organic acids may be produced which can induce weathering at great depth. For example, Ollier (1969, p. 49) reports a 6 mm diameter tap root penetrating nearly 6 m with a 30 mm weathered sheath around it, even though the surface soil was only 60 cm deep.

Organic debris clearly plays a crucial role in the development of the soil, both directly by providing one of the principal soil constituents, and indirectly by helping to weather inorganic fragments. We can only discuss the decomposition of organic material, however, when we have established its source and the agents responsible for its decay.

3.2 The origin and incorporation of organic material

Most soil organic matter is derived from plants, and its amount and form vary considerably with the type of plant formation. Two plant sources – leaf litter and decaying root systems—account for most organic material; a small contribution is made by the soil fauna. Grasslands quickly return a great proportion of their dry matter to the soil in the form of leaves and fibrous roots. Forests, on the other hand, produce a great deal of leaf litter but the woody root systems decompose slowly and are seldom available for breakdown.

In grasslands, since both roots and leaves decay readily, organic residues are provided directly, not only to the surface (as with leaves from trees), but also to the upper part of the solum (*Fig 3.1*). In woodlands the small part played by

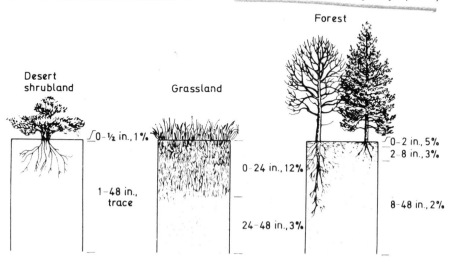

Fig 3.1   Contrasts between the root systems of desert shrubland, grassland and forest [from Hunt (1972)]

tree roots and twigs in providing organic debris means that the principal source of supply is by the incorporation of decaying leaf litter into the soil. This is mainly accomplished by the soil fauna.

Animals, notably earthworms and arthropods, in particular the mites (*Acari*) and the springtails (*Collembola*), incorporate the products of decay into the body of the soil, while the decomposition processes themselves are largely undertaken by micro-organisms. The distribution and density of these organisms in any soil is markedly influenced by moisture, acidity and temperature.

Anaerobic conditions

In anaerobic conditions many biochemical reactions are severely suppressed by the paucity of microflora, especially the fungi which are the only organisms capable of decomposing lignin. As a result, organic matter accumulates with its tissue structures more or less intact. In extreme cases the result is *peat* (§ 4.3.6).

Aerobic, acid conditions

In aerobic, acid conditions decomposition is also very slow because of the low level of microbial activity, fungi being the principal group present. Moreover, the acid-tolerant vegetation tends to be dominated by plants with a high lignin content, e.g. conifers and heath plants such as the *Ericaceae*. Lignin tends to encrust cellulose fibres in the leaf cells so that they decompose very slowly and the return of nutrients to the soil is retarded. Furthermore, in these acid conditions there are few earthworms to mix the organic and mineral fractions. The organic matter therefore tends to accumulate as a distinct horizon on the surface. Decomposition does take place, but only slowly, as the fungi are much less efficient at this task than the bacteria. However, the lower part of the organic (O) horizon is markedly more decomposed than the upper, as it has been exposed to biological attack for longer. Definite layering (*Fig 3.2*) is therefore evident in the form of:

- ● L litter horizons
- ● F fermentation horizons
- ● H humic horizons

The L layer consists of virtually untouched leaf litter representing the previous year's leaf fall. Below this is the fermentation (F) layer which contains fragmented and partially decomposed material, but with some elements of the plant structure still visible, e.g. the veins and stems. Finally, resting on the mineral soil, is the H layer which shows virtually no structure and appears to the naked eye as a black, greasy material. It is clear that such horizons form only very slowly, and Kendrick (1959) has shown that in this sort of environment it may take over nine years for pine needles to cease to be recognisable. Acid accumulations with an L, F, H sequence are referred to as **mor** (*Fig 3.2*).

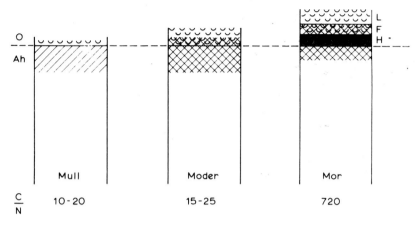

Fig 3.2   Mull, moder and mor horizons. For symbols see p. viii

Slightly acid to alkaline soils

Slightly acid to alkaline, freely draining soils show a dramatic contrast. Here bacteria and other microbes act much faster than in either of the other two sets of conditions. Not only is organic matter rapidly digested but faunal, especially earthworm, activity constantly incorporates the products of organic decay into the mineral soil. Moreover, the organic and mineral colloids are generally strongly bonded together to form stable aggregates, and distinct accumulations of organic matter are no longer visible. There may be a thin scatter of leaf litter, but this rapidly gives way to a dark brown organic/mineral horizon; the litter probably represents only the remnants of last season's leaf fall. In this **mull** type of organic matter (*Fig 3.2*) it is not possible to distinguish the structure of the digested leaves and other organic debris. It has been estimated that in these conditions oak leaves will disintegrate completely in eight or nine months [Burges (1967) p. 485].

Between the neutral or slightly acid conditions in which mull develops and the very acid conditions of mor there is an intergrade called **moder**. Although much of the organic fraction is well decomposed and incorporated into the mineral profile, the binding between the two remains weak. There is, therefore, no strong structural development, and a thin layer of litter and fermented material accumulates on the surface.

3.3   Soil organisms

It is clear from this brief discussion of the sources of organic material and the way it accumulates under different conditions that micro-organisms play a major role in the decomposition of vegetable and animal debris.

Although the main agents of organic decomposition are the bacteria and fungi, other organisms are involved in the physical and chemical breakdown of the mineral fraction. These will also be considered below.

Bacteria

These are the smallest of the soil micro-organisms, only a few microns in length (*Fig 3.3a*). Although they are the most common, on occasions reaching populations of 10^9 per gram of soil or more [Clark (1967)], they normally make up less than half the total microbial tissue of the soil. Bacteria have been found in tundra and desert soils so that it is possible that a little biochemical weathering occurs even in these extreme climatic conditions.

There are several types of bacteria, but the chemotrophic group are the most important in weathering. They are able to oxidise mineral substances to provide their energy requirements, in the course of which rock is necessarily weathered.

However, soil bacteria are generally not tolerant of very acid conditions and only a small number of species are adapted to operate in anaerobic conditions.

Actinomycetes

Actinomycetes are intermediate between bacteria and fungi, and are in many ways difficult to differentiate from bacteria. Whereas bacterial cells multiply to form clumps, actinomycetes form long filaments like fungi. They are important in the decomposition of organic matter as they use celluloses, proteins and possibly even lignin as nutrients.

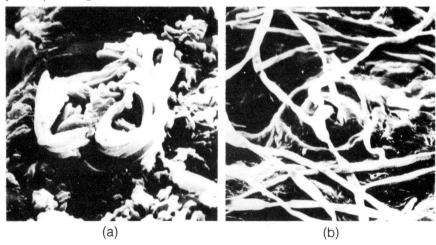

(a)   (b)

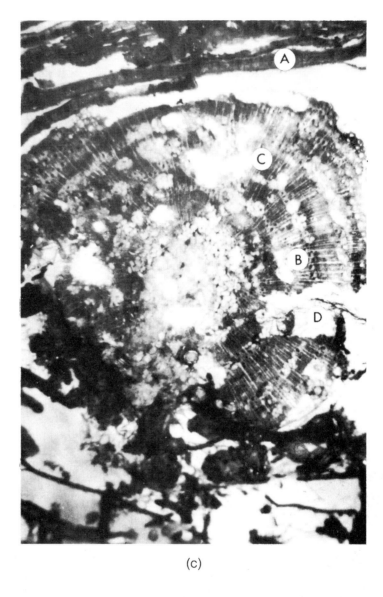

(c)

Fig 3.3   Soil organisms. (a) Bacteria on the surface of a tussock grass leaf (*Chionochloa*) x 6 000.
(b) Fungi penetrating a stomatal opening on a decomposing beech leaf (*Nothofagus*) x
3 000. (c) Cross-section of a rotting twig (10 mm diameter) in the fermentation horizon
of a beechwood moder showing (A) compact masses of sweet chestnut leaves (*Castenea
sativa*) with dark fungal stoma; (B) cryptostigmatid mite in cavity excavated by feeding
along the vessels; (C) faeces of cryptostigmata; (D) fungal hyphae innervating twig from
surrounding leaf litter

Fungi

Because of their very long filaments, which may add up to 100 m in one gram of soil, fungi probably account for the major volume of soil micro-organisms (*Fig 3.3b*). In acid environments where other micro-organisms do not thrive, fungi are the dominant agents of decay. They are also the principal consumers of lignin (*Fig 3.3c*), which encrusts the cellulose fibres in the cell wall. Their presence is therefore vital—without fungi cellulose decomposition would be impeded. Fungi are important in acid soils because of their tolerance of acid conditions, not because such conditions represent their optimum habitat.

Algae

Algae are single-celled plants, sometimes with filaments, and are primary rock colonisers. Certain species are able to attach themselves to bare rock surfaces and utilise carbon dioxide and nitrogen from the air as well as minute quantities of nutrients extracted directly from the mineral structure.

Lichens

Symbiotic growths of algae and fungi, lichens, are able to survive on an unweathered surface by extracting nutrients from the rock. For much of the time they maintain a water film on the rock surface so that inorganic weathering is promoted. They also swell on wetting and contract on drying—a process liable to break off fragments of the rock to which they adhere. It is often the decomposition of lichen which first gives a rudimentary 'litter' of organic debris on which higher plant forms may grow.

Fauna

Most fauna in the soil belong to the Protozoa (unicellular animals), Annelida (earthworms), Nematoda (unsegmented round worms) Arthropoda (insects and mites) (*Fig 3.3c*), and Mammalia (mammals). Their function is partly physical, in that they are able to move weathered materials about, and partly biochemical, in that they produce excretions with which mineral matter can be altered.

3.4   Organic matter decomposition

As we have seen, both plants and animals are responsible for providing the organic material which is ultimately incorporated into the solum. However, site conditions largely determine the way in which this material is decomposed and the extent to which it is mixed with the mineral fraction of the soil.

Immediately an organism dies the carbohydrates, protein and waxes of which it is composed come under biochemical attack. This transformation produces **humus**, a term which should be reserved for organic material at an advanced stage of decomposition. Kononova (1966) has distinguished still further between what she calls 'strictly humus substances', accounting for up to 85–90 per cent of organic matter, and those substances belonging to the well-known groups shown in Table 3.3 as 'products of advanced decomposition of organic residues'.

Table 3.3   Constituents of soil organic matter

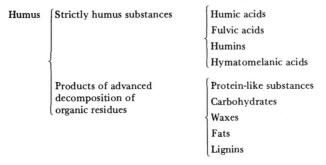

Humus ⎧ Strictly humus substances

 ⎧ Humic acids
 ⎪ Fulvic acids
 ⎨ Humins
 ⎩ Hymatomelanic acids

Products of advanced
decomposition of
organic residues

 ⎧ Protein-like substances
 ⎪ Carbohydrates
 ⎨ Waxes
 ⎪ Fats
 ⎩ Lignins

Fresh and incompletely decomposed
     plant and animal
     residue

[source: Kononova (1966) p. 48]

Before the decomposition of fresh organic matter is studied in detail it is useful to consider the nature of these 'strictly humus substances'. Their structure and even their existence have been under investigation since the early nineteenth century, though their complexity and, in many cases, their strong linkages with other components of the soil system have made them singularly difficult to understand. Many humic substances have been recognised, but recently, with the development of new ideas and techniques, a broader view of their structure has been taken and there is now a widespread belief that all display similar chemical structures. Indeed, most are thought to be variants of the humic acids.

All strictly humic material (the first group in Table 3.3) consists of very large molecules of high molecular weight. Recent work suggests that these are formed by the aggregation (polymerisation) of considerable numbers of constituent molecules, which can be thought of as the basic building blocks. These building blocks appear to be of two main types:

● aromatic ring structures (*Fig 3.4*), based on the familiar benzene (C_6H_6) ring; usually this is either a polyphenol in which hydroxyl (OH) groups have replaced some of the hydrogen (H) in benzene, or of a quinoid nature in which some of the sites are occupied by oxygen

- nitrogen-containing compounds: either ring structures or linear chains, mainly proteins, amino-acids and saccharides

To explain the differences between the groups of humic substances we must look at the way the two structural units are linked together. First, the detailed composition of the individual molecular building blocks will vary according to the site conditions and the nature of the fresh organic matter from which they were derived. Secondly, they may combine in varying ratios. Thirdly, environmental conditions can influence the end-product by controlling the removal of the by-products of polymerisation.

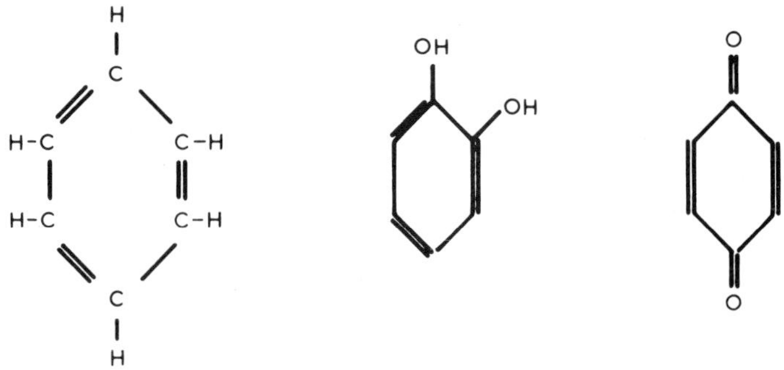

Benzene

Pyrocatechol
(polyphenol)

Quinone

Fig 3.4   The structure of benzene, pyrocatechol and quinone

With these considerations in mind we can now look at the differences between the major groups of humic material. These can be viewed as a series, at one end of which are the **fulvic acids** which are weakly polymerised. In this case relatively few constituent molecules have linked together. They are also weakly 'aromatised'—the dominant components are the nitrogen-containing chains, rather than the ring structures. At an intermediate stage of development are the **brown humic acids** while in the **grey humic acids** polymerisation is strong and aromatisation is dominant. Although these acids are presented here as belonging to distinct groups, they should really be seen as a system of polymers displaying continuous variation.

Strictly humic substances thus possess fundamentally similar structural properties, although, as will be shown later, as far as soil formation is concerned each group behaves in quite different ways.

Having discussed in very general terms the structure of these humic substances, we can now investigate the way the primary organic matter—leaf litter, root material, animal residues and faeces—is transformed into humus.

It will help if we consider organic decay as occurring in two stages. In the first stage, largely soluble organic compounds of simple structure are formed along with purely mineral compounds and gases. This is usually called **mineralisation.** In the second stage, strictly humic material, mainly colloidal and insoluble in water, is formed, a process known as **humification** (*Fig 3.5*).

SOIL ORGANIC MATTER

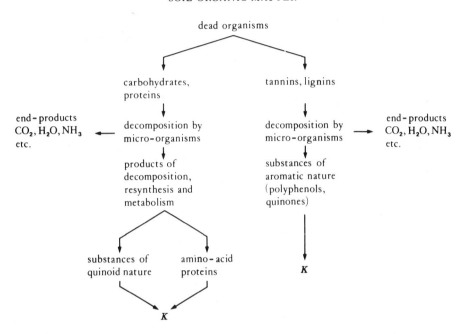

Fig 3.5   Possible ways of forming humic substances during the humification of plant residues (K=condensation)
[source: Kononova (1966)]

3.4.1   Mineralisation

The main products of this first phase of decomposition are displayed in very simplified form in Table 3.4. We must consider the decomposition of the three principal organic fractions—celluloses, lignin and protein—under constrasting conditions:

- aerobic with a pH above 5.5
- aerobic with a pH below 5.5
- anaerobic

Table 3.4   Principal products of biochemical mineralisation of primary organic matter

	Aerobic environment (pH>5.5)	**Aerobic environment (pH<5.5)**	**Anaerobic environment**
Organisms involved in decay	Bacteria Fungi Actinomycetes	Fungi	Bacteria Actinomycetes
Organic matter			
Cellulose and sugars	CO_2 Cellular carbon Polyphenols	CO_2 Cellular carbon Polyphenols	CO_2 Hydrogen Ethyl alcohol Methane Ethane Simple organic acids (e.g. acetic)
Lignin	Humin	Monomers of polyphenols	Hardly changed
Protein	Nitrites Nitrates	Polyphenol-tannin-protein complex Very slow production of ammonia	Strong ammonia production Little nitrification

Principal products from other sources:
- from leaf drip — polyphenols
- from microbial secretions — polysaccharide gums, humus and protein-like substances

Aerobic with pH above 5.5

Well drained soils which give a neutral to alkaline reaction are biologically active. Good examples of such soils are the freely draining chernozems (Mollisols) of the North American prairie and the Ukrainian steppe or the rendzinas (Rendolls) of the chalklands of south-east England and the Paris basin (see Chapter Six). These soils contain large populations not only of macro-fauna such as earthworms and arthropods, but also of micro-organisms. In these biotically active conditions mineralisation can proceed apace. A wide range of soluble and gaseous products of simple structure form from the carbohydrates and lignin. These mineralisation products are subsequently humified (see below). The primary protein, on the other hand, is successively transformed (*Fig 3.6*) into amino-acids and ammonia and then nitrified by bacteria to produce nitrites and nitrates. It is in the latter form that nitrogen can be assimilated by growing plants. In addition, wherever micro-organisms are active they will produce secretions, notably polysaccharide gums and humus-like substances.

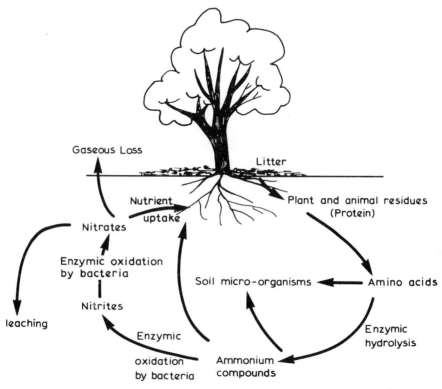

Fig 3.6   The nitrogen cycle

Aerobic with pH below 5.5
Contrasting with the rapid mineralisation which occurs in biotically active environments is the much slower rate of decomposition in more acid, although still aerobic, conditions. As we have seen in § 3.3, this can be attributed largely to the high lignin content of much of the litter and the small bacterial population in soils of low pH. Accordingly, most of the mineralisation is performed by the fungi.

However, there are certain other important characteristics which distinguish mineralisation in acid environments from that in more nutrient-rich areas. In particular, the polyphenols (*Fig 3.4*) (produced by the breakdown of celluloses and lignin) do not, in this case, transform rapidly into humic acids. Instead they form stable, resistant complexes with protein, protein conversion to ammonia is minimised, and there is virtually no production of nitrates for plants.

Fig 3.7   A peat soil, Plynlimon, central Wales

The resistant polyphenol-protein complex is also important in impregnating cellulose cell membranes. This reduces the rate of cellulose mineralisation, further encouraging litter accumulation. These processes are dominant in the podzols (Spodosols) which form on the heathlands of Atlantic Europe and under the coniferous forests of Canada and Siberia (see Chapter Six).

Anaerobic

Anaerobic conditions are found extensively on river flood plains with a high water table, in areas of high effective rainfall, such as the western hills of Ireland, and in areas of poor site or soil drainage such as the Canadian Muskeg. Again, as in acid soils, the population of micro-organisms, especially fungi, is extremely low (*Fig 3.7*), but here mineralisation is achieved by certain anaerobic bacteria and actinomycetes. The end products are quite different from those found in aerobic environments. Celluloses are mineralised to give mainly gaseous products which provide no 'building blocks' for subsequent humification. Although ammonification of protein is strong, the low population of nitrifying bacteria means that nitrification is minimal. Thus the great bulk of organic residue after mineralisation consists of lignin or lignified tissues which suffer very little chemical change, although some polyphenols may be released. In extreme circumstances of saturation this residual material accumulates to considerable depths to form peat.

3.4.2 Humification

Mineralisation is only the first stage in the decomposition of raw organic matter. It produces soluble constituents of simple structure. The next stage is humification, in which large molecules of complex structure, generally colloidal and of low solubility in water, are produced: the constituent molecules produced in mineralisation—aromatic compounds of polyphenol nature and nitrogen-containing chain compounds—are linked together (polymerised). In a comparison of soils from Saskatchewan Anderson (1979) has argued that this polymerisation involves the initial creation of high molecular weight materials. Subsequent humification results in an increase in the aromatic element but a decrease in molecular weight. Again the environment exercises a marked control on the speed of the reactions and the nature of the end-products.

In biotically active conditions with a neutral/alkaline reaction polymerisation is rapid and strong with the formation of colloidal grey humic acids, typical of mull (p. 45). Coulson *et al.* (1960) have demonstrated that the transformation of polyphenols to grey humic acids is favoured by the abundance of Ca^{2+}.

In well-aerated acid soils polyphenols are produced, particularly during the mineralisation of lignin. However, subsequent humification is restricted so that weakly polymerised fulvic acids and brown humic acids are produced, and then only slowly. Polyphenols therefore tend to accumulate in such acid soils, which is very important in podzolisation (see § 4.3.4).

A similar picture can be painted of humification in anaerobic soils. Aeration is widely held to be essential for the disposal of the by-products of polymerisation. Without it polymerisation itself cannot proceed effectively, and only fulvic acids and sometimes brown humic acids are produced. In acid peats and gleys polyphenols again accumulate.

Duchaufour (1976) has demonstrated that the extent to which humic material is transformed depends very much on the effectiveness of 'stabilising agents' and on 'insolubilisation' by mineral cations. The most important stabilising agent is calcium carbonate, which he believes protects organic matter against microbial degradation by shrouding it in a carbonate film. This could be one reason for the very high levels of little-changed 'inherited lignin' found in rendzinas. Amorphous alumina may behave in a similar way, although not with fresh organic residues. In addition, alumina, along with calcium carbonate and active free iron, can be instrumental in 'insolubilising' humic compounds as humic acids or humins.

The formation of grey humic acids and polysaccharide gums is vital in maintaining strong aggregates [Duchaufour (1968)]. As we have seen, their production is favoured by:

- a high level of biotic activity
- alternating wet and dry conditions

In opposite conditions polymerisation is slow and weak and accompanied by the accumulation of polyphenols. Unless polysaccharides continue to be produced, the majority will be decomposed, like other carbohydrate material.

A central process in the decomposition of organic matter is the production of mineral nitrogen from protein. As the carbon content of humus is determined initially by the composition of the fresh organic matter, we can use the C/N ratio to show how far mineralisation and humification have proceeded. Humus formed by rapid decomposition with the production of high levels of N will be typified by a low C/N ratio of about 10. This is the case with calcareous mull, i.e. mull in which the complex is dominated by Ca^{2+}, as under calcareous grassland or on a calcareous parent material. At the other extreme, under heathland and coniferous woodland, where slow nitrification leads to the production of mor, the C/N ratio may increase to 20–30. Forest mull and moder have an intermediate position on the scale.

This discussion of humification has concentrated on the details of the process. However, it should be appreciated that the nature of the products of humification directly affects the behaviour of the mineral fraction, and in particular the development of structural aggregates or peds (§ 2.7). Grey humic acids form very large polymers, and flocculate rapidly in the presence of Ca^{2+}. In contrast brown humic acids, and especially fulvic acids, remain in a dispersed state. Soils in which grey humic acids dominate therefore tend to develop strong aggregates while the reverse holds for soils containing the more weakly polymerised humic material.

3.4.3 Summary of processes in the decomposition of organic matter

Organic matter is important for several reasons:

- it provides bonding agents which give strength to the soil structure
- it provides nutrients for further plant growth
- during decomposition it yields soluble substances which help to differentiate horizons

Two stages are involved in organic decomposition:

- mineralisation, involving the breakdown of primary organic debris by micro-organisms and the production of simple soluble substances and gases
- humification, in which some of the soluble mineralisation products link together to form very large and usually insoluble molecules, which we know as humus

Mineralisation, essentially a biochemical process, varies in both rate and form according to the types of micro-organisms present. Some, in particular the bacteria, are very sensitive to the acidity and oxygen levels in the soil. Decomposition tends to be most rapid in those biotically active environments which are aerobic and have a high pH, while under acid litter (such as is produced by heath plants or conifers) or in anaerobic conditions, the pace of breakdown is retarded because organic decomposition is left almost entirely to the fungi. Fungi are not nearly as efficient at this as bacteria, and at times decay almost comes to a standstill. Debris then accumulates in which the original structures may be quite evident for very long periods.

Humification can best be summarised as a polymerisation process in which some of the soluble products of mineralisation (notably polyphenols and nitrogen-containing compounds) link together to form very large, often insoluble, molecules. These behave as colloids in much the same way as the clay minerals to which they are often strongly bonded. However, humification is ineffective unless the soil shows a neutral/alkaline reaction. In biotically active soils humic colloids will form rapidly, but where it is acid or anaerobic the process slows down, and the intermediate, soluble products of mineralisation (especially the polyphenols) remain. As we shall see, this can lead to podzolisation.

4. Soil-forming processes

4.1 Introduction

Ever since the work of Dokuchaev in the late nineteenth century, it has been appreciated that soil is a result of the interaction of **climate, vegetation, animal organisms** and the mineral **parent material**. It was later recognised that **topography** is also important and that the whole process of interaction needs to be related to the **time** available for soil formation.

If we examine the interaction of these **pedogenic factors** we can recognise three fundamental processes:

- the decomposition of organic matter and its incorporation into the mineral profile (as discussed in § 3.4)
- the *in situ* weathering of mineral matter in the solum (*Fig 1.2*)
- the translocation of material, both in solution and in colloidal suspension

These transform what would otherwise be an inert parent material into a dynamic soil in which distinct horizons can be recognised.

4.2 Weathering in situ

Some soils develop with very little vertical movement of material, i.e. simply by weathering. Such soils have in common a high level of biotic activity and parent materials which yield a large quantity of polyvalent cations or sesquioxide colloids. Such conditions are found with calcareous parent materials where Ca^{2+} is released and also in some conditions where Al^{3+} is released. The high level of biotic activity is also important in returning to the surface any soluble constituents that have been leached. These soils have an ABwC profile, usually with merging horizons.

So far we have seen weathering essentially as a process providing parent material upon which the soil-forming (pedogenic) processes can work. However, weathering clearly does not cease at this stage: hydrolysis, hydration, etc. proceed unabated in the solum and often produce their own distinctive horizon arrangements. Depending on the relative strengths of translocatory movements and weathering, the latter may be the dominant pedogenic process. In certain soils translocation may be suppressed because the aggregates possess strong water stability and so do not disintegrate readily. If this is so, the clays are unlikely to be moved. In these circumstances we can recognise weathering *in situ* as a pedogenic process in its own right. However, it is critical to establish the circumstances under which aggregates retain their strength and stability.

4.2.1 Temperate climates

In discussing weathering *in situ* in temperate climates it is helpful to consider two contrasting groups of parent material:

- calcareous
- acid

Calcareous environments
On calcareous material, such as the colluvial chalk 'head' of southern and eastern England or the tills of Wisconsin age in southern Ontario, high levels of exchangeable calcium encourage the flocculation of clay and humic colloids. In base-rich conditions a high level of bacterial activity produces polysaccharide gums which give strength to the aggregates (§ 3.4). The calcareous mull typical of these soils is characterised by intimate, strong bonding between the mineral fraction, especially the silicate clays, and the organic material. These factors help to develop strong, water-stable structural units and therefore to suppress translocation, especially of the clays and the sequioxides.

Acid environments
Rather surprisingly, stable structures may also form in some acid environments, such as on parent materials derived from granites, gneisses and certain sandstones. In these cases it is not Ca^{2+} but ions of the iron and aluminium families which cause flocculation. Duchaufour and Souchier (1978) have placed great emphasis on the role of active free iron which occurs as films around clay particles and links them to humus. They argue that a high iron content is essential for the formation of a mull humus in the soils they investigated in the Vosges. Furthermore, they believe that the formation of stable aggregates depends upon at least a minimal percentage of clay—*c.* 5 per cent, in their experience. There is certainly general agreement that iron and aluminium perform a critical function in acting as bridges between the clays and the humus to provide a stable crumb structure, even in an acid

environment. However, the humus is not well protected against biological decomposition, so the turn-over of organic matter is substantial.

These acid soils are commonly mantled by forest mull derived from broad-leaved deciduous litter. Unlike most of the profile, this mull accumulation may be only slightly acid; this is probably largely due to the herbaceous ground vegetation which, with its shallow fibrous rooting system, retains and recycles the metallic cations and other nutrients within the superficial layer. There is therefore likely to be a high level of biotic activity, especially of earthworms, in the upper horizons. Any colloidal material which may have been translocated stands a good chance of being returned to the surface. Moreover polysaccharide gums, produced as bacterial secretions, give strength to the aggregates.

Even though there is very little movement of constituents in these soils a clear horizon pattern can usually be seen. This is typically of ABwC form. The Bw (or **cambic**) horizon is here the main zone of intense weathering and, whether the soil is calcareous or acid, it displays certain common characteristics. Both the primary material (coarsely weathered rock fragments) and the products of intense chemical attack (the clay minerals and sesquioxides) are found in this horizon.

However, distinct forms of Bw horizon are possible:

● the production of quantities of clay minerals in a zone below that of extensive root growth often results in the development of prismatic or blocky structures which contrast sharply with the granular or crumb peds of the A horizon. We call this a 'Bw structural' horizon

● where the parent material is iron-rich, considerable amounts of ferric oxide may be liberated by hydrolysis and hydration to give a rich rust colour to the cambic horizon. We call this a 'Bw colour' horizon

4.2.2 Seasonally contrasting hot climates

In the processes discussed in Chapter Two, the weathering of the primary minerals—notably by hydrolysis—takes place under acid conditions, which can be ascribed to high levels of dissolved CO_2 and the production of simple, soluble organic acids during the mineralisation of organic matter. Generally speaking, the more intense the weathering, the more acid the soil water. In the tropics and sub-tropics, however, CO_2 levels in the weathering zone are much lower than in more temperate climates, and in these conditions there is a strong affinity between the Al and Si produced by hydrolysis. Accordingly silica-rich clays—micas and montmorillonite—form. Furthermore, mineralisation products seldom survive for very long before they are humified, so the possibility of iron movement is minimal, and iron accumulates in many tropical soils giving a characteristic red colour to the soil.

However, iron is not only found in considerable quantities, it is also distributed within the soil in a distinctive form. The liberation of iron under these conditions is in many ways a specific case of weathering *in situ*, but it is convenient to think of it as a definable process—**rubefication**—in which lowly hydrated oxides are dispersed throughout the soil, giving it a brilliant red hue. However, as with many other processes, it rarely operates independently, and rubefied soils often also show signs of lessivage or ferrallitisation (§§ 4.3.3 and 4.3.7). Rubefication is dependent on certain combinations of site conditions—in particular of parent material and microclimate.

Rubefication is usually found on calcareous parent materials, although it has also been reported on schists and basalts. These materials can yield soils with a high level of base saturation (pH close to 7). This is not to say that the limestones provide calcareous soil material. In fact, all the free carbonates have usually been removed, leaving a residue of silicate impurities. Nevertheless, under these conditions of near-neutrality hydrolysis of the ferromagnesian minerals liberates iron which is very soon immobilised, as there are few chelating agents (§ 4.3.4) at hand. Aluminium oxides and silica are also produced during hydrolysis, but they resynthesise immediately to form clay minerals. This weathering process therefore results in two components: iron oxides and clay minerals, both of which are colloidal but carry opposite charges. Consequently strong bonds develop between them, to such an extent that the two fractions are almost inseparable.

However, as the name suggests, it is the colour of rubefied soils which is their principal hallmark. It is a common belief that the intense red colour (Munsell hue 2.5YR or redder) can be attributed to strong seasonal desiccation, which transforms the liberated iron oxides to the anhydrous form, hematite (Fe_2O_3), which is a bright rusty red. But Segalen (1971) has suggested that these brilliant colours (Plate 1) are due to a mixture of goethite (FeO.OH) and the amorphous oxides which are sometimes referred to as limonite. Despite this uncertainty it is clear that rubefication is dependent on a wet season, when hydrolysis can operate, alternating with a warm, dry period during which stable ferric oxides are formed.

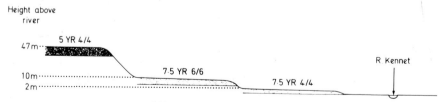

Fig 4.1   A cross-section of the terraces of the river Kennet, Berkshire, showing variations in sub-soil colour. The gravels of the 47 m terrace are thought to date from the Anglian cold period while those of the 10 m terrace have been assigned to the Wolstonian cold period; the 2 m terrace is of Upper Devensian age

At present, we can only be certain that the process
restricted mountainous areas of the Mediterranean lands
America. Many of the rubefied soils of the tropics, such as a
in west and east Africa, are thought to be palaeosols.
deposits in western Europe show evidence of rubefication bu
from the mid- or even the early Pleistocene (*Fig 4.1*).

4.3 Translocation

In some places the only process operating is weathering *in situ*, but most soils
are a response to processes which redistribute at least some of the components
within the soil system. These movements are called **translocation** and are of two
types:

- **leaching,** which is the movement of materials downwards or laterally in
  solution
- **eluviation,** or the physical movement of material in suspension (some
  authors have grouped both types of translocation under eluviation)

Translocation can only become important when the effectiveness of agents
which cause aggregation or which behave as cements is reduced.

Although many substances within the soil are soluble in water and can be
leached, they are not all equally so. The salts, especially chlorides and
sulphates, of sodium and potassium are most soluble. The calcium and
magnesium salts, in particular the sulphates and carbonates are less soluble.

Eluviation depends entirely on the disintegration of the peds. For this to
occur the agents which behave as cements or which cause flocculation must be
removed or replaced. There are four basic cementing or flocculating agents (§
2.7):

- the exchangeable cations of which the polyvalents are the most effective in
  bringing about the flocculation of organic and clay mineral colloids; Ca^{2+}
  and Mg^{2+} are the most common in most soils
- the positively charged colloids of iron and aluminium oxides, which play a
  similar role in acid conditions
- the free oxides of iron and aluminium and calcium carbonate which are
  able to form 'bridges' between silt and sand particles (*Fig 2.16*)
- humic material, especially the polysaccharides, which, it is thought,
  provides one of the main bonds in holding together 'constructional'
  aggregates [Russell (1971)]

We will consider a sequence of soil-forming processes which represent increasingly effective leaching and disintegration of the aggregates and, therefore, progressively more severe translocation. Although presented as distinct processes, each is simply a variation in the intensity of operation of common physical and chemical changes, involving the weathering process described in Chapter Two and movement of material in solution and colloidal suspension.

The principal movements in some of the processes are shown diagrammatically in *Fig 4.2*. These processes will not all be dealt with to the same extent, and we concentrate on those with which the reader is likely to be confronted, in particular those operating in areas of so-called temperate climates.

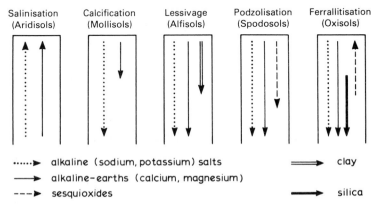

Fig 4.2   The range of soil translocation processes

Fig 4.2 shows that of the processes to be discussed only salinisation and ferrallitisation – associated mainly with tropical climates – involve any upward translocation of soil components.

4.3.1   Salinisation

The salts of sodium and potassium are particularly soluble and therefore mobile. In moist climates they are removed from the soil completely and carried away in the ground-water. In arid and semi-arid conditions, although they may be taken into solution, they remain within the profile. This applies especially where there is a source of *saline* ground-water close to the surface. With a low suction prevailing near the water table and the surface horizons, desiccated by evaporation, being at a high suction, upward movement can take place. As the saline solution evaporates, crystals of sodium chloride form white **efflorescences** in the upper part of the profile (*Fig 4.3*).

Environments suitable for this process are not uncommon. They are found in coastal areas where the ground-water may be contaminated with sodium salts, e.g. along the Mediterranean shores of Languedoc in southern France, or where the parent material is derived from evaporite formations, e.g. in South Alberta and Death Valley, California (i.e. former playa lakes). Areas of closed drainage, in particular, often display the most effective salinisation.

Fig 4.3   A puff-solonchak from Iraq. The light-coloured undulating surface is dominated by saline efflorescences, whilst other saline deposits can be seen within the upper mineral soil

Whatever the source of the salt, salinisation usually occurs in depressions, where the ground-water is most likely to be close enough to the surface. The soil solution will, in most instances, contain not only sodium chloride but also salts of the alkaline earths, especially calcium. Being in dilute solution, these dissociate into their constituent ions, thus providing the cations which will largely determine the stability and form of the peds. Where calcium salts are present in solution the adsorbing complex is, for the most part, saturated with Ca^{2+} ions, and so the upper horizon remains flocculated and a stable structure results. Only when the level of adsorbed Na^+ reaches very high levels, and especially when the soil solution becomes very diluted, as often occurs in irrigation projects, do the clays disperse and the structure collapse.

It should be evident that this process can operate wherever the hydrological and climatic conditions and the parent material are appropriate. It is not confined, therefore, to the hot arid areas of the world: the semi-arid areas of Soviet Central Asia and Iran show salinisation and related processes operating most effectively. Furthermore, Claridge and Campbell (1968) have observed saline accumulations even in polar desert soils in parts of Antarctica. However, not even a majority of semi-arid and arid soils are saline.

4.3.2   Calcification

Under less arid conditions than are associated with salinisation where there is, over the year as a whole, a moisture surplus, the more mobile, soluble constituents (sodium, potassium) move down through the profile rather than to the surface. In the grasslands of the continental interiors—the North American prairie, the Soviet steppelands and the grasslands of New South Wales and the pampas—sodium salts are generally leached deep into the profile and removed in the ground-water. On the other hand, the less soluble calcium compounds are mobilised but reprecipitate lower in the soil, possibly as a Bca or Cca horizon.

Because of the strong biological activity in these soils, considerable carbon dioxide, CO_2, is liberated by respiration. This enables calcium carbonate to be converted into the soluble bicarbonate which can move down through the profile:

$$CaCO_3 + H_2O + CO_2 \rightleftharpoons Ca(HCO_3)_2$$

In areas of low rainfall and grassland cover, reprecipitation is encouraged by:

- a decline, with depth, in biological activity and, therefore, in CO_2 content
- evaporation which affects much of the profile during the prolonged periods of dry weather

The above reaction is then reversed with the formation of secondary deposits of crystalline calcium carbonate (calcite) sometimes as infilled animal burrows or filaments (**krotovina**). Other calcium salts are also precipitated, the depth at which this occurs depending on their mobility. Thus deposits of calcium sulphate are often found below the zone of carbonate accumulation. This is the process of calcification—the first, and least severe, of a series involving the downward movement of materials.

A similar process operates in some brown calcareous soils (Ochrepts). These frequently occur in western Europe and in the north-eastern United States on transported calcareous parent material such as loess or head. Here the secondary accumulations often appear as krotovina in the Bw (cambic) horizon. It is likely that these have formed around existing fibrous roots, since their tubular structure can be clearly seen.

Although the A horizon is largely decalcified during this process (i.e. the free calcium carbonate is removed), the clay-humus colloids remain saturated with Ca^{2+} ions. This is partly because the extensive fibrous root systems of herbaceous plants take up much of the leached material and return it to the surface of the soil as leaf litter. As we have seen, saturation of the colloids with Ca^{2+} helps to maintain water-stable aggregates and this is further encouraged by the polysaccharides (§ 2.7) produced by the large population of micro-organisms in these biotically active soils.

The downward movement of carbonates may be one of the processes in the formation of calcareous duricrusts or **calcrete**. However, the amount of carbonate is much greater than could have been provided by the present overlying soil, and so it seems certain that other processes must be involved and that many calcretes are at least partly fossil.

4.3.3 Lessivage

Under a temperate climatic regime, a change in vegetation to deciduous woodland coupled with an increase in the effective rainfall markedly alters the type of translocation. Deciduous woodland, as we have seen, tends to generate an acid (*c*. pH 5) forest mull or moder humus. Also, as the effective rainfall increases, so does the effectiveness of leaching. Carbonates are not merely moved into the lower horizons, they are totally removed from the system. Furthermore, the increased passage of hydrogen ions through the profile leads to the **acidification** of the upper horizons of the soil. Conditions such as this have obtained throughout much of the late Holocene, for instance, over the north European plain, the north-eastern states of the USA, the St Lawrence lowlands and parts of southern Australia.

The increased concentration of hydrogen ions in the soil water has the following results:

- cation exchange takes place on a large scale so that the dominance of Ca^{2+} on the colloids is now replaced by that of H^+. The acidity of the soil may increase to pH 6 or even 5—hence the application of the term acidification to this process. Ca^{2+} is thought to be one of the more effective agents in flocculating clay and humic colloids, (§ 2.7) and its replacement by H^+ results in a relative dispersion of the aggregates in the upper horizons.
- there is a coincident decline in the activity of micro-organisms, particularly bacteria. Thus the rapid production of humic material and gums found under grassland does not occur under the more acid

conditions normally associated with deciduous woodland. Either not enough is produced of the humic material which bonds together the fine mineral particles, or it is itself mineralised into soluble forms – another and more telling reason for the collapse of the aggregates

● there is a limited formation of mineralisation products, particularly polyphenols and fulvic acids, which further affects the stability of the peds, since these substances can dissolve the iron and aluminium compounds which form bridges between individual mineral particles (*Fig 2.16*)

Thus, with increasing acidity, the water stability of the aggregates decreases because of:

● deflocculation
● mineralisation of humic cements
● dissolution of ferric and aluminium hydroxide cements

As the bonds between individual sand, silt and clay particles are loosened, they are free to be eluviated, provided the pores are large enough for them to pass. Clay and to a lesser extent silts are, therefore, the principal fractions which are mobilised. Generally the clays will slake most readily when the soil is first wetted after a dry spell. It is this dismemberment of the aggregates and the movement of fine material in suspension which is called lessivage.

Where and in what form is the mobilised clay redeposited? It is now generally accepted that much of the clay which is eluviated from the upper (Eb) horizon accumulates lower down the solum in a B horizon. This is commonly referred to as the Bt or B-textural horizon, indicating that it is differentiated from the material above and below it on the grounds of texture (*Fig 4.4*). In the US

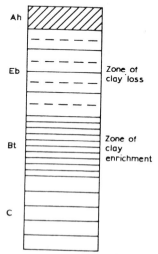

Fig 4.4   The essential features of a profile subject to lessivage. For symbols see p. viii

Department of Agriculture System of Soil Classification [US Soil Survey Staff (1975)], it is described as an **argillic** horizon.

Much of the progress in recognising the diagnostic characteristics of these accumulation horizons has been made through microscopic analysis of thin sections of undisturbed soil. When viewed under the microscope (*Fig 4.5*) the clay accumulations appear as fluidal structures lining the major voids. These accumulations are known as **clay-skins** or **cutans** [Brewer (1964)]. The clay crystals are oriented in a sub-parallel fashion about the ped so that when viewed under a hand lens, or even with the naked eye, the clay skin appears shiny.

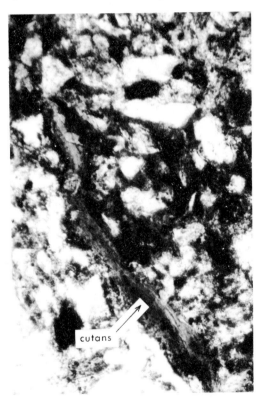

cutans

Fig 4.5   Lessivage as seen under a microscope. The elongated soil pore running from top to bottom of the photograph is seen to be lined with clays showing preferred orientation (cutans). These are readily differentiable from the more diffuse clay domains which form the matrix between the sand grains in the remainder of the photograph

The immobilisation of clay in the Bt horizon is controversial. Some argue that the dispersed clay reflocculates because of an increase in the concentration of exchangeable Ca^{2+} with depth (i.e. increasing pH). Others consider that the dispersion of the aggregates in the Eb horizon is largely attributable to the breakdown of the clay-humus bonds, and that lower down the profile in the Bt horizon, as polymerisation proceeds, a strong linkage develops which stabilises and immobilises the clay. It has also been suggested that clay may be immobilised in the zone of maximum penetration of summer rainfall – a zone which often coincides with the limit of fibrous root systems. Finally, the translocated clays may be held together on the peds during desiccation, which allows van der Waals' forces to come into play.

In the discussion so far it has been tacitly assumed that variations in clay percentage with depth (*Fig 4.4*) can be explained simply in terms of clay eluviation. However, Oertel (1968) and Brewer (1968) have shown that this is not necessarily the case. The 'excess' of fine material in the Bt horizon is frequently far too great to be accounted for by eluviation, and it is most likely that much of the clay found in the Bt horizon comes from weathering *in situ* (§ 4.2). If this is the case, it well illustrates the fact that more than one pedogenic process can operate in one soil at the same time.

Lessivage generally takes place under deciduous woodland where there is a moderate effective rainfall. However, if we turn our attention to soils under coniferous woodland or ericaceous heath, especially where there is a high leaching effectiveness, we find a much more severe process of translocation—podzolisation.

4.3.4   Podzolisation

Lessivage, as we have seen, involves the translocation of silicate clays in colloidal suspension without any change in their chemical composition. A far more serious disruption takes place when the clay minerals decompose and the hydrous oxides of iron and aluminium are mobilised. This is podzolisation. There are three distinct processes involved:

- decomposition of the silicate clay minerals, principally kaolinite, montmorillonite and the micaceous clays
- mobilisation of the hydrous oxides of iron and aluminium, together with silica
- reprecipitation of the oxides (to give the characteristic rust-red accumulations) in the Bs horizon (Plate 7), and the reformation of clays in this horizon.

These processes also explain the formation of the bleached Ea horizon in the upper part of the profile (*Fig 4.6*)

In general, podzolisation is associated with highly acid environments, such as heathland or coniferous woodland, where quantities of soluble organic components are produced (§ 3.4), and resistant and humified material remains as the mor accumulation. The soluble products are mainly the polyphenols and carboxylic acids, such as citric and oxalic acids.

Coulson *et al.* (1960) have demonstrated that we must look to these compounds to understand the three processes listed above; the lowly polymerised fulvic acids may also be involved.

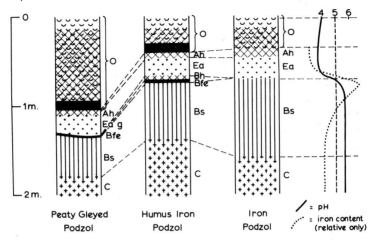

Fig 4.6   The major variations in podzol profile morphology. For symbols see p. viii

Decomposition of the silicate clay minerals
As acidification increases, the clay minerals break down into their constituent parts based on the silicon-oxygen tetrahedron and the alumina octahedron. Ponomareva (1969, p. 94) has suggested that montmorillonite is particularly soluble in fulvic acids, but even kaolinite, normally regarded as a more stable constituent, is markedly unstable.

In temperate climates it appears that montmorillonites and the micaceous clays are destroyed by the opening up of the plates, and alumina is liberated. At the same time, silica is released from the tetrahedral layers in a colloidal form. If conditions are favourable, both the alumina and the silica move through the profile into the B horizon where they may precipitate separately or resynthesise to form new clay materials, probably resembling kaolin.

Mobilisation of the hydrous oxides of iron and aluminium
The decomposition of the silicate clays yields silica and free alumina, and weathering of the primary minerals produces hydrous iron oxides; these are the basic components involved in podzolisation.

Atkinson and Wright (1957) showed that the passage of pure water will not lead to the segregation of iron and aluminium within the profile which is seen in podzolic soils. But Coulson *et al.* (1960) demonstrated conclusively that the mobilisation of iron and aluminium (which Bloomfield was able to achieve with leaf leachates in his experiments in the 1950s), can be attributed to water-soluble products of organic decomposition. Polyphenols, dissolved both from living leaves and fresh leaf litter, are particularly effective. However, fulvic acids and some simple acids, such as citric and oxalic acids, can play a similar role.

The free oxides of iron and aluminium react with these organic constituents to form soluble metal-organic complexes—a process known as **chelation**. In this way the weathered mineral constituents in the upper horizons of the soil are largely mobilised. This process can take place even in conditions of near-neutrality, as Bloomfield (1954) has demonstrated, using an aqueous extract from fresh aspen litter. However, at pH 7 chelation can scarcely be maintained and this may be related to the processes of immobilisation discussed below.

The removal of iron and aluminium creates an ashen Ea horizon, depleted of all but the highly resistant grains of quartz. Without their mantle of ferric oxide these grains appear bleached—this can readily be seen, even in a hand sample in the early stages of podzolisation.

Precipitation of hydrous oxides

Although the accumulation of hydrated oxides of iron is the most obvious characteristic of the lower part of a podzolic profile, other morphological features are associated with it—particularly the occurrence in humus-iron podzols (Orthods) (see p. 112) of a zone of organic accumulation (Bh horizon) immediately above the Bs sesquioxide accumulation.

It should be remembered that iron and aluminium are mobilised when they form soluble complexes with organic constituents such as polyphenols and relatively simple organic acids. A ferric-organic complex is first formed but this is almost immediately reduced to a soluble ferrous-organic complex. Bloomfield's (1953) classic experiments showed that while iron in the form of a ferrous-organic complex was soluble, with time ferric iron was formed which even at pH 4.5 precipitated out. Drying out and oxidation during the summer may then yield the oxides of iron and an insoluble polymer, probably akin to the humic acids. That immobilisation may occur because of oxidation on drying is suggested by the fact that iron accumulations in podzolic soils are often coincident with a layer of coarse-textured material—a well-aerated zone where oxidation may be expected to be most active. However, Evans and Adams (1975) found that in podzolic soils in mid-Wales much of the aluminium taken into solution was not retained within the soil.

Once sesquioxide deposits have been initiated in the B horizon the process is largely self-perpetuating, since the ferrous-organic complex can be absorbed, as Bloomfield (1955) initially suggested, on to the existing nucleus of ferric hydroxide, where it is oxidised. If immobilisation operates in this way the secondary iron and polymerised organic material should be closely associated. This can easily be shown to be the case.

In experiments involving aqueous extracts from mor horizons, Bruckert and

Jacquin (1969) were able to show that certain organic acids of low molecular weight—notably citric, oxalic and malic acids—are much more capable of dissolving iron than the strongly polymerised humic acids. Furthermore, they may migrate further down the profile before they are polymerised and precipitated out, which could explain the differentiation of the B horizon.

Schnitzer and Skinner (1963) have pointed to the significance of the molar ratio of the metals to organic matter. With metal/organic ratios of less than 1:1, both iron and aluminium remain in solution, but precipitation of the hydrous oxides becomes universal when the metal/organic ratio reaches 6:1.

Over the last twenty-five years it has become clear that chelating agents play a central role in mobilising the hydrous oxides of iron and aluminium. The subsequent polymerisation of these agents with nitrogen-containing compounds may be involved in the redeposition of the oxides in the B horizon.

4.3.5   Gleying

In podzolisation the movement of the hydrous oxides of iron and aluminium generally takes place where there is free drainage. This is usually under conifers or heathland plants which provide quantities of the necessary chelating agents. However, movements of iron can occur to a limited extent even in soils which, through poor drainage, are anaerobic. These movements, and the conversion of ferric (III) to ferrous (II) compounds, are called gleying.

Wherever the entry of oxygen into the soil is impeded, the processes described above are complemented, and sometimes replaced, by gleying, in which the rusty colours so typical of freely draining soils are replaced by the ochres, greens, blues and greys associated with such compounds as ferrous phosphate and ferrous sulphide. However, in most cases only part of the profile is dominated by these hues, and there is a mottled zone in which ferrous compounds account for the subdued colours while oxidised ferric

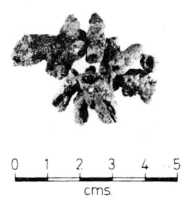

```
0   1   2   3   4   5
cms.
```

Fig 4.7   A tubule

minerals—particularly goethite and lepidocrocite—produce the yellowish-brown mottles. Sometimes the iron becomes markedly segregated to give local concentrations of ferric iron, often in the form of nodules or other indurated forms such as tubules (*Fig 4.7*). These concentrations suggest that where gleying takes place there is some movement of iron compounds. This will be discussed below, but we will consider the environment in which gleying operates before the details of the process.

Gleying can usually be attributed to the permanent or temporary saturation of at least part of the soil profile. There are several situations in which this may happen. In basin depressions and flood plains the ground-water table may be high enough to produce anaerobic conditions throughout much of the profile (**ground-water gleying**). Imperfect drainage within the soil because of a horizon of low permeability can also lead to gleying (**surface-water gleying** or **stagnogleying**). However, saturation is not in itself enough to transform ferric to ferrous compounds (reduction). This is only possible when dissolved oxygen levels within the soil water have fallen critically. Both higher plants and micro-organisms play a part in this as they utilise dissolved oxygen, creating the truly anaerobic conditions in which reduction can take place. If the soil water is constantly and rapidly renewed by rainfall, gleying rarely occurs, since oxygen levels remain high. Clearly gleying is not confined to any one climatic 'zone'. We shall see in Chapter Six that gleyed soils are found in the tropics, the Arctic, the continental interiors and the oceanic margins.

The 'umbrella term' of gleying shelters various component processes:

- reduction of ferric compounds
- translocation of iron as ferrous compounds or complexes
- precipitation of iron as mottles and minor indurations

In voids, where the supply of oxygen is small, it may rapidly be depleted by uptake through root hairs. Severe local anaerobic conditions may arise, and these will be evident in the grey and green colours of the void margins (Plate 6).

Although the reduction of iron to a ferrous state can be caused simply by an oxygen deficit, Bloomfield (1951) demonstrated conclusively that soluble organic chelates from fresh leaf litter strengthen the process considerably.

Although the reduction of iron compounds is an essential part of the gleying process, one must not assume that no translocation is involved. It is now widely recognised that in gley soils iron is able to migrate both on a micro- and on a macro-scale and in some respects there are notable similarities between the translocation of iron in podzolic soils and gleys. In particular, the mobilisation of iron as soluble ferrous-organic complexes, especially under the action of polyphenols (p. 49) and fulvic acids, is closely paralleled in podzolisation.

Nevertheless, there are important differences. Bloomfield (1951) observed that peds derived from soils at Rothamsted Experimental Station displayed distinct concentric zones of iron enrichment and depletion (*Fig 4.8*). This would suggest a process of diffusion, in which iron is dissolved from the outer 'shell' and translocated as ferrous iron towards the centre of the ped where it is reprecipitated. The precise mechanism of immobilisation is not clear, but sorption on to existing nuclei of hydrous ferric oxides may be involved. The depletion of the iron content of the outer layers of the structural units thus explains the grey (gleyed) ped surfaces so commonly seen in seasonally hydromorphic soils. The scale of the movement of iron compounds is usually very small, in most cases only a matter of a few millimetres. However, the fact that some long-distance migration does take place is shown by the accumulations of rusty deposits in some field ditches on flood plains. This can be seen very clearly during the spring months when the water level is high and there is a rusty film on the water surface.

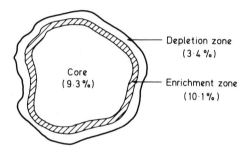

Fig 4.8   Concentric zones of gleying in a ped; iron content expressed as $\%Fe_2O_3$
[based on Bloomfield (1951)]

Thus the immobilisation of iron may occur through sorption on to existing nuclei of hydrous ferric oxides, forming mottles or even concretions. These mottles are often of the mineral lepidocrocite, $FeO(OH)$, which is widespread in soils subject to waterlogging [Brown (1953)]. However, the accumulation of ferric oxides, frequently seen on the flanks of major voids, requires a different explanation. It seems likely that ferrous iron in solution diffuses to the soil/air interface, from which the iron is precipitated on contact with oxygen, often as tubular concretions lining major voids.

Two points are worth noting:

● the diffusion and precipitation are extremely slow, so that noticeable accumulations only form where the voids are aerobic for several months and where the air-water interface remains at or about a constant position
● only the major voids—notably root channels and earthworm burrows—are likely to contain the oxygen necessary for tubular concretions to form

To summarise: gleying must *not* be regarded simply as the production of grey, green and blue ferrous compounds resulting solely from a dearth of oxygen in waterlogged conditions—that is, a static process. It should be seen as the reduction and solution of iron, partly because of a lack of oxygen in the soil water and partly under the influence of organic chelating agents, followed by translocation—often micro, but sometimes macro in scale—and the reprecipitation of these iron compounds.

On sites subject to even higher rates of water reception than those which give rise to gleying, soil formation is dominated by the accumulation of organic material on the surface (peat formation).

4.3.6 Peat formation

Wherever the upper soil horizons remain saturated for most of the year it is very likely that processes of mineral alteration and translocation will be replaced by organic accumulation and the formation of peat.

Conditions favourable to the maintenance of saturation occur in several situations. We have seen that valley bottom sites are often associated with soils which are gleyed throughout almost the whole profile. If the water table rises into the O horizon for much of the year anaerobic conditions will be found there too. Organic decay will be retarded and ultimately a **basin peat** may form. This also often happens on plateau surfaces where water disposal is impeded. On the other hand, where the effective rainfall is sufficiently high, e.g. in western Ireland, organic debris may remain saturated from this source alone – the accumulation being referred to as **blanket bog**. Thus there are two principal causes of saturation of the O horizon:

- a very high water table
- high effective rainfall (i.e. heavy rainfall coupled with low evapotranspiration) and poor water disposal

There are also occasions when parent materials, or even soil-forming processes, may create a similar effect to that produced by relief and climate. For example, the development of a lowly permeable clay-rich horizon such as the Bt of a sol brun lessivé (Udalf) or a pan in a podzolic soil (Spodosol) can impede drainage to the extent not only that the profile is gleyed but that there may also be peat formation.

As shown in § 3.4, the pattern of organic matter decomposition under anaerobic conditions is very different from that where there is free drainage. In comparison with aerated soils the total number of micro-organisms is very small indeed. A low level of biotic activity necessarily means that organic matter is broken down extremely slowly. In acid, nutrient-deficient (oligotrophic) conditions peat accumulates principally from the debris of

Sphagnum mosses and *Polytrichum* (starwort), and also from purple moor grass (*Molinia caerulea*), heather (*Calluna vulgaris*) and the heaths (*Erica* spp) which colonise the marginally drier sites. Although the bulk of the accumulation consists of the resistant lignin fraction, in these acid conditions even some of the cellulose survives microbial attack. The profile therefore often contains many easily recognisable fragments of plant tissue.

By contrast, in nutrient-rich (eutrophic) mires there is commonly a lush carpet of sedges (especially *Carex panicea* in Scotland) and mosses (such as *Campyllium stellatum*). Under attack from anaerobic bacteria the celluloses decompose completely to yield gases, particularly methane (CH_4) and carbon dioxide (CO_2), and acids, notably acetic acid. The latter are reducing agents and may encourage gleying in the mineral soil below.

In both eutrophic and oligotrophic conditions peat accumulation can therefore be rapid—in the former mainly because of the lush vegetative growth, in the latter because of the incomplete decay of the litter, particularly the celluloses.

Once established, organic accumulation is in many respects self-perpetuating. For example, because of the lack of water movement, not all the products of the micro-organisms or of organic decay are removed. The medium thus becomes polluted with these materials, some of which are toxic, so that the population of micro-organisms is further reduced. Once a thick mat of partially decomposed mosses has formed, water is retained as by a sponge. It has been calculated that *Sphagnum*, for example, can retain between ten and twenty times its own weight in water. Such factors combine to produce what are often remarkably rapid rates of peat accumulation. For instance, in a study of British post-glacial hydroseres, Walker (1970) estimated the modal rate of accumulation of bog peat to be between 51 and 60 cm per 1000 years. However, such figures conceal a huge variation in calculated rates.

The vegetative composition of a peat from base to surface is rarely uniform throughout, since the common bog plants are remarkably sensitive to variations in hydrology, which, in basin peats, can be modified substantially as the peat surface rises above the water table. Likewise a small change in effective rainfall may seriously affect the composition of the plant community. In Britain on acid peats with generally saturated conditions *Sphagnum*, the bog moss, is commonly found along with *Molinia caerulea* (purple moor grass), cotton grass (*Eriophorum angustifolium*) and deer grass (*Tricophorum caespitosum*) as well as numerous sedges. Where conditions are drier, perhaps where the bog surface is locally raised, heather (*Calluna vulgaris*) and the cross-leaved heath (*Erica tetralix*) appear. If the plant remains are sufficiently well preserved to be identified, it is possible to build up a picture of the variations in local hydrology throughout the period of peat growth by examining a peat section. Further indications of past changes are revealed by the colour and degree of humification of the peat. It is generally true that in oligotrophic peats pale yellow, little humified, spongy material forms under conditions of extreme saturation and, therefore, rapid accumulation. In contrast, dense, dark, well-humified remains can usually be attributed to a hydrologically drier period when more complete mineralisation and humification took place.

4.3.7   Ferrallitisation (lateritisation, latosolisation)

Although soil formation in the tropics is basically dependent on the same weathering and translocating processes as in more temperate latitudes, there are differences in their relative strengths. Generally speaking, chelation is not as effective as in podzolisation, especially in the lower horizons of the solum, largely because the soluble products of mineralisation are rapidly humified.

In areas which at present enjoy an equatorial climate with a mean annual rainfall of about 2000–6000 mm (80–240 in.) and soil temperatures in the vicinity of 25 °C (77 °F), weathering of the primary minerals is rapid and complete, and the more soluble weathering products—including silica—are moved from the seat of weathering, either vertically or downslope. This combination of intense weathering and efficient removal is called ferrallitisation. There are widely believed to be three basic aspects to the process:

- intensive and continuous weathering of the parent material, involving the release of iron and aluminium oxides and silica, as well as of bases
- translocation of soluble bases and silica
- formation of 1:1 kaolin-type clays

However, work by Pidgeon (1976) on ferrallitic soils in Uganda suggests that the principal pedogenic processes there are clay translocation and the alteration of the soil structure. Illuviation cutans, occupying just under 2 per cent of the total soil volume, were particularly striking in these soils.

Extremely deep sola are common in equatorial regions, because of the rapid breakdown of the rock. The active weathering horizon is therefore often far away from the zone of infiltrating rainwater, which contains organic acids and chelating agents. Furthermore, even on acidic materials, the release of cations during weathering prevents a dramatic decline in the pH [Duchaufour (1970) p. 346]. These circumstances ensure that the weathering horizon is much less acid than in the equivalent shallower soils in temperate climates. In the relatively mildly acid conditions found even on acid parent materials, the primary mafic minerals weather rapidly to release the hydrous oxides of iron and aluminium as well as silica and the metallic cations. As *Fig 4.9* shows, amorphous silica is quite soluble even at pH 5–7, so that it is taken into solution and much of it is removed in the ground-water. Alumina and the ferric oxides are virtually insoluble in this pH range and they rapidly crystallise and remain in place. However, further transformations are closely dependent on the nature of the parent material.

Basic rocks, such as basalt, are relatively low in silica, which is rapidly liberated by weathering and can be removed in the ground-water. Unless more silica is supplied from upslope, the residuum becomes dominated by ferric oxide (goethite) and aluminium oxide (gibbsite). This is true ferrallitisation, i.e. total desilicification with only the crystalline oxides remaining. A clear distinction can be drawn, therefore, between ferrallitisation and rubefication, in which the alumina and silica immediately resynthesise to give secondary clay minerals.

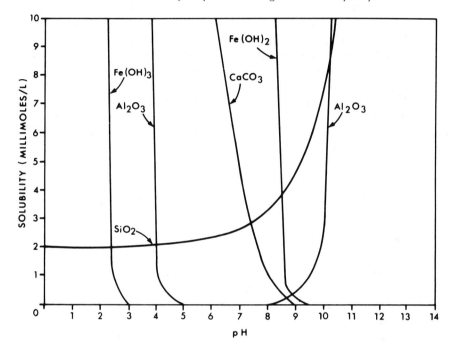

Fig 4.9   Variations in solubility of SiO2, Al2O3, Fe(OH)2, Fe(OH)3 and CaCO3 with pH [source: Loughnan (1969)]

However, ferrallitisation on acidic rocks such as granite is similar to rubefication since, despite the removal of much of the silica from the solum, considerable reserves remain which link with the alumina to form kaolin-type clays. 1:1 clays are only formed where the soil reaction is markedly acid (see § 2.3), and the weathering zone (C horizon) is close to neutrality, even on acidic rocks. Kaolin formation is, therefore, not likely here. However, immediately above this there is a zone (*Fig 4.10*) which is leached of bases and thus provides a suitable environment for kaolin synthesis. This is the **mottled zone**, which may become totally dominated by these secondary clays.

Perhaps the most favourable conditions for the formation of kaolinite are on plains where the slow movement of ground-water prevents over-rapid removal of the dissolved silica. The mottled zone also appears to be best developed where drainage is poor. Mohr *et al.* (1972) have supported the idea that the formation of kaolin may lead to gleying, especially during the wet season. As we have seen in § 4.3.5, iron will migrate from places where the reduction-oxidation (redox) potential is low, to areas of high redox, such as near pores where there may be some oxygen. Nevertheless, the reasons for the formation of a mottled zone are still very controversial.

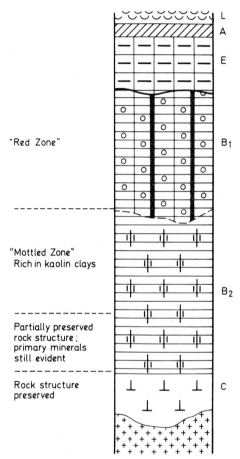

Fig 4.10   The essential features of a ferrallitic soil. For symbols see p. viii

Many of the areas where ferrallitisation is currently active have been geologically stable for an extremely long time. They have escaped the glacial events which disturbed or destroyed soils in more temperate lands, so that soil formation may well have been active throughout the Pleistocene and for much of the Tertiary. When considering soil formation on this time-scale we must obviously relate the pedological processes we have just discussed to geomorphic changes. While clays and sesquioxide colloids have been forming in the solum the landforms have been adjusting to the base-level.

In a landscape of low relief it is unlikely that all the rainwater will be removed during the wet season [van Schuylenborgh (1971)]. We have already seen how a temporary water-table may be established in the zone of kaolinisation, and how local migrations of iron and, for that matter, manganese, may take place. Iron may also concentrate in this zone by migration on a rising water table. In the horizons above the highest position of the ground-water there is little opportunity for reduction, and ageing and crystallisation of the accumulated oxides can take place. Over time a highly indurated horizon, now called **plinthite**, but for a long time known as **laterite**, may form. When the ground-water level falls because of stream incision, this layer will grow in thickness. It also seems clear that this material is transformed into a hard, resistant ironstone or **duricrust**, but opinions differ as to whether this is a natural continuation of the migration of the hydrated oxides or whether it depends on the exposure of plinthite to the air. The latter view is well summarised in *Fig 4.11* [from Ahn (1970)] where dissection of a landscape of low relief exposes the plinthite by erosion of the upper horizons. Once exposed it hardens irreversibly to provide resistant cappings to the plateau surfaces. The sharp excavator tine marks shown in *Fig 4.12* would be unlikely to be formed if the excavator were working in hard, indurated ironstone, but would result if, at the time of working, the horizon was a compact clay.

Ferruginous crusts are a characteristic feature of much of the African landscape, especially in areas which now experience a tropical climate with wet and dry seasons and are extensively pedimented. Dowling (1966) describes one from the Fika-Nafada area of northern Nigeria. It is a red *surface* sheet about 10 ft (3 m) thick and with a hard, coarsely nodular and vesicular character, frequently pisolitic (i.e. having concentric iron concretions). This layer rests directly on the Kerri Kerri massive pale-yellow sandstone.

In equatorial regions it has often been observed that ferrallitic soils which are characterised by malleable clay-rich horizons (the mottled horizon) when under forest cover often degenerate and become concretionary after burning and subsequent grass (savanna) vegetation. These concretionary horizons have very similar characteristics to the hard crusts often found in the drier tropics. The elevated plains which the ironstone crusts mantle may be late Tertiary, or possibly even older [King (1962)], which would suggest that the crusts too may be of great age. If this is so, it follows that the ironstone crusts are the product of a different period of pedogenesis from that affecting the lower areas.

Conditions towards the surface of the soil tend to contrast markedly with those found in the weathering zone. Generally speaking, the litter produced by the trees of the equatorial forest gives an acid reaction, especially on acid parent

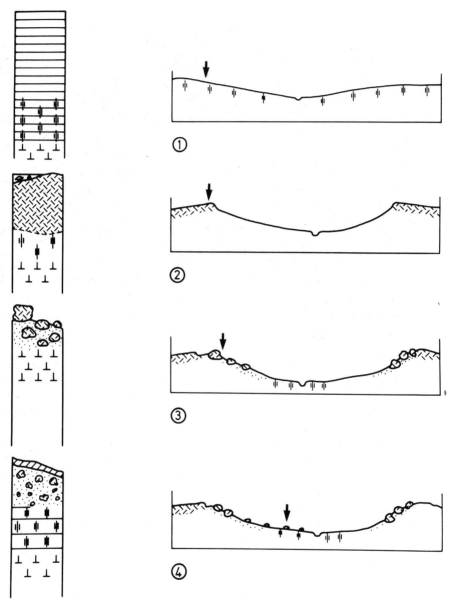

Fig 4.11   Possible stages in the formation of ironstone crusts from the formation of a mottled
subsoil (1) which becomes indurated (2) and later exposed at the surface consequent on
erosion (3). This crust hardens and is then eroded (4) to provide the concretions in a
later profile in which the sequence is repeated. Possible landscape changes are shown
alongside. For symbols see p. viii
[source: Ahn (1971)]

Fig 4.12   A vesicular ironstone crust (with tine marks), Imala, south-west Nigeria

materials, and a process similar to podzolisation takes place. Even kaolin is unstable, and the colloidal silica which is released can migrate down the profile. Furthermore, the soluble products of organic decomposition tend to polymerise only slowly, and as a result the oxides of iron and aluminium are mobilised by chelation. But it is only in iron-rich soils subject to seasonal changes in moisture content that these elements appear to accumulate. Under these climatic conditions the rapid crystallisation of iron during the dry season can cause a mutual precipitation of the alumina and silica as reformed kaolin in the B horizon [Duchaufour (1968) p. 81].

5 Classification and mapping of soils

5.1 Introduction

Soils vary continuously from place to place because of the changing importance of the various soil-forming processes. This results in a continuum of soils, often with no marked boundaries. Nevertheless, certain distinct types of soils can be recognised and attempts have been made to categorise world soils.

Of the major classification systems, that of Sibertsev (1899) (Table 5.1) which developed out of the ideas of Dokuchaev (1886) has become widely known and is based largely on environmental controls. It introduces the term **zonal soils**, referring to the fact that the distribution of the soils described largely coincided with climatic zones.

Other workers tried to classify soils on the basis of their profile characteristics. Marbut's scheme (Table 5.2) illustrates this approach. The initial breakdown was into **pedocals** (soils with free calcium still in the profile) and **pedalfers** (those without).

The most recent attempt to produce a detailed and comprehensive classification has been made in the United States (Table 5.3) and is called the 'Seventh Approximation'. In an attempt to escape from the confusion associated with traditional terminology, this system has introduced a whole range of new terms. It develops further the tendency to rely on profile characteristics rather than on environmental controls.

Systems whose origins may be traced to Dokuchaev or the Seventh Approximation are both in current use and have been referred to throughout this book along with the scheme adopted by the authors (Table 5.7).

An ideal soil classification should be suitable for use by the surveyor in the field as well as the compiler of world soils maps. As more detail is required for larger-scale projects, so finer divisions are needed in the classification. In most cases soils mapped in the field are classified on the basis of a unit called a **soil series**. In traditional hierarchical classifications, these series are grouped

progressively to produce more widely defined units suited to mapping larger
areas at smaller scales.

5.2   Classification

It should be evident from the previous chapters that, with so many processes
operating with differing degrees of intensity across the world's land surfaces, the
contrasts between soils will be vast. There will be soils on clays which are
waterlogged and subject to gleying, while others close by on gravels may be
freely drained and heavily podzolised. Elsewhere—and especially in the
tropics—deep weathering over a long period may have produced a profile rich
in kaolin and sesquioxides, while in Arctic and alpine localities soil
development may consist of just a few millimetres of weathered material
overlying the bedrock. There is continuous variation in soil properties between
the extremes.

Grouping together similar soils may suggest relationships with
environmental controls such as vegetation or parent material. Indeed,
Dokuchaev's classification of Russian soils in the late nineteenth century
demonstrated very clearly that soil types tended to be associated with particular
climatic zones.

However, certain major problems have troubled pedologists ever
since Dokuchaev [Kellogg (1974)]. If soils occurred in discrete units,
classification would pose few problems, but as they are more like a spectrum,
the selection of class limits inevitably involves arbitrary and, therefore,
debatable decisions. However, change in soil character is sometimes sharp
enough to enable certain boundaries to be established, which provide the basis
for classification. Pedologists, like biologists, have generally developed this
simple one-tier grouping into a hierarchical system. The units at the lowest level
are amalgamated to form larger, and therefore more variable groups at the next
level, and so on. This approach has been used in virtually all classifications from
the early attempts of the Russians to the American's Seventh Approximation
[US Soil Survey Staff (1975)] and the system advanced for use in Britain by
Avery (1973).

No system suitable for, say, an agronomist will be of equal value to an
engineer or a geomorphologist. In other words, no system can be described as
'general purpose'. Most of the systems referred to in this book are primarily
pedological: they have been produced with soil-forming processes and
environmental relationships in mind. They also have some agricultural value.

Initially, soils were grouped according to either their texture, or the
geological formation on which they developed. Thus Hall and Russell referred
to 'soils of the Gault Clay', etc., in their *Report on the Agriculture and Soils of Kent,
Surrey and Sussex* (1911). This system continued in use in Britain [e.g. Pizer

(1931)] long after the pedological approach of Dokuchaev had been widely adopted in other parts of Europe and North America.

Dokuchaev (1886) had realised that soil horizonisation resulted from the interaction of various environmental controls. In particular, the early Russian workers soon saw that there was a strong correlation between bioclimatic zones and the freely draining soils of an area, and so the concept of **zonal soils** was developed. Freely draining soils (Table 5.1) were described as normal or zonal (each associated with a particular bioclimatic area). Inevitably similar soils forming under diverse climates, for instance those in which there is a strong influence of parent material, did not fit comfortably into this system and were, therefore, referred to as **intrazonal soils**. These characteristically show well-developed horizons, in which they differ from the third category of **azonal soils**. Into this class were put those which displayed only embryonic pedogenic development, such as recent alluvial and aeolian materials. This approach clearly places much emphasis on environmental associations and it has been the basis of the geographical approach to pedology ever since, especially in the USSR [see, for instance, Gerasimov and Glazovskaya (1965)]. However, it tends to overstress the importance of climate and vegetation and results in the classification of bioclimatic phenomena rather than the soils themselves.

Table 5.1   Classification of world soils by Sibertzev (1899)

Normal or zonal soils (i.e. dry land vegetative soils)

Zone	Soil type
Boreal	Tundra (dark brown) soils
Taiga	Light grey podzolised soils
Forest-steppe	Grey and dark grey soils
Steppe	Chernozem
Desert-steppe	Chestnut and brown soils
Desert zone	Aerial soils, yellow soils, white soils
Sub-tropical and tropical forest	Laterite or red soils

Transitional or intrazonal soils

Dry land moor soils or moor-meadow soils
Carbonate-containing soils (rendzinas)
Secondary alkaline soils

Abnormal or azonal soils

Moor soils
Alluvial soils
Aeolian soils

Table 5.2   The classification of soils according to Marbut

Category VII	Category VI	Category V	Category IV	Category III	Category II	Category I
Pedalfers	Podzolic soils	Tundra, Podzols, Brown forest soils, Red soils, Yellow soils, Prairie soils		Soils with perfectly developed profiles / Soils with imperfectly developed profiles	Soil series groups (a very great number)	Soil units based on texture of surface horizon
	Lateritic soils	Laterites, Ferruginous laterites				
Pedocals	Pedocals of temperate zone	Mid-latitude temperate zone; Northern temperate zone; Southern temperate zone	Chernozem, Chestnut coloured, Brown, Grey	Soils with perfectly developed profiles / Soils with imperfectly developed profiles	Soil series groups (a very great number)	Soil units based on texture of surface horizon
	Pedocals of tropical zone	The various still unknown groups of tropical pedocals	Various sub-groups none of which have yet received distinctive names			

[based on Marbut (1928) p. 17]

Between the wars there was a move away from this approach to one which placed more emphasis on genesis and profile characteristics. Marbut's (1928) classification (Table 5.2) typifies this change in emphasis. He also developed the idea of a hierarchical scheme much further than any of his predecessors. A basic division was made between soils with free carbonates in the solum (**pedocals**) and those profiles dominated by the hydrous oxides of aluminium and iron (**pedalfers**). This generally coincides with the boundary between leaching excess and evaporation excess (expressed annually). By sub-dividing these fundamental categories the hierarchy shown in Table 5.2 was constructed. At the lowest level (soil type) the classification also provided the basic field mapping unit for survey work. However, Webster (1968) has argued that soils by their very nature are not amenable to hierarchical classification, and that the only satisfactory approach is one which is essentially single-tier.

As soil-forming processes became better understood more emphasis was placed on them in classification. Kubiëna (1953), a prominent pedologist, based his taxonomy on horizon organisation (Table 5.3). He defined horizons, often quite loosely, in terms of certain diagnostic characteristics, considered to be major responses to the principal soil-forming processes. Thus major units were defined in terms of profile organisation, e.g. ABwC, AC profiles. Within each class he harked back to environmentalist thinking by recognising sub-aqueous, semi-terrestrial and terrestrial soils. Specific individual properties are neither necessary nor sufficient for class membership. It is thus a flexible system, since a soil is not automatically excluded from membership of a class by the lack of just one of the many characteristics of that class. With complex bodies such as soil profiles this is a desirable characteristic. In Europe, the stress placed by Kubiëna on horizon organisation has been taken up by several survey organisations and individuals. Duchaufour (1970) in France has adopted a similar approach while Fitzpatrick (1967) in the UK has developed the idea much further.

There has been a gradual shift of emphasis, at least in western Europe and North America, away from environmentally orientated systems to those more reliant on soil morphology. This trend is epitomised by the Seventh Approximation produced by the US Soil Survey Staff in 1960 and finalised in 1975, after extensive collaboration with other overseas surveys (Table 5.4). Its curious title reflects the succession of drafts and modifications produced by the Survey before its final publication. It is definitely one of the most comprehensive and universally applicable systems ever devised, and is intended to apply not only to soils of the continental United States but also to those of tropical areas. It is traditional in approach in that it encompasses six levels ranging from **Orders**, with only ten classes, to **Series** which provide the basis for field mapping. At the higher levels the properties which define each unit are very carefully spelled out. Although clear definition is welcome in some respects, it has proved to be one of the major points of criticism. We have already suggested

Table 5.3   Classification of European soils by Kubiëna (1953)

(A)C soils

Very weakly developed soils with soil life only in a thin upper layer; lacking distinguishable humus layers
Main groups: raw soils, Arctic raw soils, desert soils

AC soils

Soils lacking a B but with distinct organic stained or humic horizon
Main groups: rendzinas, rankers

ABwC soils

Soils in which the B horizon is due to weathering and not to the translocation of material
Main groups: brown earths, red earths, *terra rossa*

ABC soils

Here the B horizon contains not only weathering residues but also illuvial material, e.g. clays, carbonates
Main groups: leached brown soils (sols lessivés), podzols

B/ABC soils

Associated with areas of strong moisture deficit; illuvial movements are toward the surface where a surface crust may form
Main groups: surface crust soils

(N.B. Only terrestrial soils have been cited in this table)

that material as complex and variable as soil must possess several properties before it can be allocated to any particular class. However, the lack of the occasional attribute should not exclude the soil from that class. In general, the Seventh Approximation does not permit such flexibility, nor, in certain cases, does it allow for normal sampling errors in the determination of the various attributes. These are serious deficiencies in a system which at the same time has many good points. For instance, by the introduction of a completely new terminology—some might call it jargon—it has eliminated much of the confusion which surrounded such terms as 'brown forest soils' and 'latosols'. Although at first sight a little bewildering, the terminology is easy to understand once the principles of its construction have been grasped. This may be illustrated by reference to Orders and Sub-orders. The name of each Order is based on syllables which are intended to convey the major attributes of that class. Ultisols result from a long period of weathering and translocation involving the depletion of base reserves and the movement of clay—hence the use of the element *Ult* (-imate). To construct class names at Sub-order levels, two formative elements are taken—the first indicating characteristics of the soil or its environment (such as *aqu*, indicating wetness), the second being a suffix derived from the name of the Order. Thus we could have the Sub-order Aquults. The formative elements are shown in Table 5.5.

Table 5.4   US Department of Agriculture classification — the Seventh Approximation (1975)

Order	Sub-order	Characteristics/environment
Alfisols (soils with an argillic horizon and moderate to high base content)	Aqualfs	with gleying features
	Boralfs	others in cold climates
	Udalfs	others in humid climates (including most leached brown soils)
	Ustalfs	others in sub-humid climates
	Xeralfs	others in sub-arid climates
Aridisols (desert and semi-desert soils)	Argids	with argillic horizon (i.e. zone of clay accumulation)
	Orthids	other soils of dry areas
Entisols (immature, usually azonal soils)	Aquents	with gleying features
	Arents	artificially disturbed
	Fluvents	on alluvial deposits
	Psamments	sandy or loamy sand textures
	Orthents	other Entisols
Histosols	Fibrists	plant remains very little decomposed
	Folists	freely draining Histosols
	Hemists	plant remains not recognisable because of decomposition. Found in depressions
	Saprists	plant remains totally decomposed (black)
Inceptisols (moderately developed soils, not in other orders)	Andepts	on volcanic ash
	Aquepts	with gleying features
	Plaggepts	with a man-made surface horizon
	Tropepts	in tropical climates
	Umbrepts	with an umbric epipedon (i.e. dark coloured surface horizon of low base status); hills and mountains
	Ochrepts	other Inceptisols (including most brown earths) of mid — high latitudes
Mollisols (soils with a dark A horizon and high base status e.g. chernozems, rendzinas)	Albolls	with argillic and albic horizons
	Aquolls	with gleying features
	Rendolls	on highly calcareous materials
	Borolls	others in cold climates
	Udolls	others in humid climates
	Ustolls	others in sub-humid climates
	Xerolls	others in sub-arid climates
Oxisols (soils with an oxic horizon or with plinthite near surface)	Aquox	with gleying features
	Humox	with a humose A horizon
	Torrox	Oxisols of arid climates

Table 5.4   continued

Order	Sub-order	Characteristics/environment
	Orthox	others in equatorial climates
	Ustox	others in sub-humid climates
Spodosols (soils with accumulation of free sesquioxides and/or organic carbon e.g. podzols)	Aquods	with gleying features
	Ferrods	with much iron in spodic horizon
	Humods	with little iron in spodic horizon
	Orthods	with both iron and humus accumulation
Ultisols (soils with an argillic horizon, but low base content)	Aquults	with gleying features
	Humults	with a humose A horizon
	Udults	others in humid climates
	Ustults	others in sub-humid climates
	Xerults	others in sub-arid climate
Vertisols (cracking clay soils with turbulence in profile)	Torrerts	usually dry (cracks open for >300 days per year)
	Uderts	usually moist (cracks open and close several times per year)
	Usterts	cracks remain open >90 days per year (in monsoon climates)
	Xererts	cracks remain open >60 days per year

The whole system relies on the recognition of key or diagnostic horizons—some of them surface and others sub-surface. We can summarise the characteristics of the principal sub-surface horizons as:

Albic horizon: clay and free iron oxides have been removed, so the colour is determined by the colour of sand and silt particles themselves.

Agric horizon: an illuvial horizon rich in clay and/or humus formed under and compacted by cultivation.

Argillic horizon: contains substantial amounts of illuviated clay.

Calcic horizon: a horizon more than 15 cm thick containing secondary precipitations of $CaCO_3$.

Cambic horizon: an altered horizon (usually resulting from weathering), characterised by distinctive structures, clay formation or liberation of free iron oxides.

Gypsic horizon: as calcic horizon, but precipitations are of $CaSO_4$.

Natric horizon: an argillic horizon with columnar structures and more than 15 per cent saturation with Na^+.

Oxic horizon: contains very few weatherable minerals and clay is almost exclusively as kaolinite or sesquioxides.

Placic horizon: a thin black to dark reddish pan cemented by iron, manganese or an iron-organic complex.
Salic horizon: as gypsic horizon, but salts present are more soluble than gypsum.
Spodic horizon: contains accumulations of free sesquioxides and/or humus, but not of silicate clays.

Table 5.5   Formative elements in names of Sub-orders of Seventh Approximation

Formative element	Meaning
alb	presence of albic horizon (a bleached eluvial horizon)
and	ando-like (i.e. volcanic ash materials)
aqu	characteristics associated with wetness
ar	mixed or cultivated horizon
arg	presence of argillic horizon (a horizon with illuvial clay)
bor	of cool climates
ferr	presence of iron
fibr	fibrous
fluv	flood plain
fol	presence of leaves
hem	presence of well-decomposed organic matter
hum	presence of horizon of organic enrichment
ochr	presence of ochric epipedon (a light-coloured surface horizon)
orth	the common ones
plagg	presence of a plaggen epipedon (a man-made surface > 50 cm thick)
psamm	sandy texture
rend	rendzina-like
sapr	presence of totally humified organic matter
torr	usually dry
trop	continually warm
ud	of humid climates
umbr	presence of umbric epipedon (a dark-coloured surface horizon)
ust	of dry climates, usually hot in summer
xer	with annual dry season.

In the years which have elapsed since its introduction the system has gained widespread acceptance, although enthusiasm for it remains lukewarm in some quarters.

The Soil Map of the World, initiated by FAO/UNESCO in 1961, had to be based on a universally acceptable classification. After discussions and revisions the final definitive version was published in 1974 [FAO/UNESCO (1974)]. Although this classification is being used for the World Map project the terms defined have not so far come into general use and will not, therefore, be enlarged upon here.

The difficulties of producing a classification which is universally acceptable and applicable are well illustrated by the development of the system adopted by the Soil Survey of England and Wales [Avery (1973)]. As with recent trends in the USA and the Netherlands, this scheme (Table 5.6) relies on specific soil properties to define class limits. However, whereas attributes such as the texture of the soil material were regarded as subsidiary in the Seventh Approximation, a Major Group of cracking clays (pelosols) has been separated out by Avery. Perhaps the most obvious difference is the importance assigned to gley soils which account for two of the ten Major Groups in the English scheme. Contrast this with the Seventh Approximation where gleying is only taken account of in the second level of the hierarchy.

There are many reasons for these divergences between the various schemes, but we can isolate two main underlying factors. One is the increasing

Table 5.6   Classification of Soil Survey of England and Wales

Major group	Sub-group	Characteristics/environment
Terrestrial raw soils (mineral soils with no diagnostic pedogenic horizons)	Raw sands	non-alluvial, sandy
	Raw alluvial soils	on alluvial deposits
	Raw skeletal soils	on bedrock or fragmental material
	Raw earths	on unconsolidated loams or clays
	Man-made raw soils	on artificially disturbed material
Hydric raw soils (gleyed mineral soils, normally in very recent marine or estuarine alluvium)	Raw sandy gley soils	in sandy material
	Unripened gley soils	in loamy or clayey alluvium
Lithomorphic (A/C) soils (soils with distinct, humose or organic topsoil over C horizon)	Rankers	with non-calcareous topsoil over bedrock
	Sand-rankers	with non-calcareous, non-alluvial C horizon
	Ranker-like alluvial soils	in non-calcareous recent alluvium
	Rendzinas	over very calcareous fragmentary limestone
	Pararendzinas	over moderately calcareous C horizon
	Sand-pararendzinas	over calcareous sandy C horizon
	Rendzina-like alluvial soils	in recent alluvium
Pelosols (slowly permeable, cracking clays)	Calcareous pelosols	calcareous, but without argillic horizon
	Non-calcareous pelosols	non-calcareous and without argillic horizon
	Argillic pelosols	with argillic horizon

Table 5.6   continued

Major group	Sub-group	Characteristics/environment
Brown soils (soils excluding pelosols with Bw or Bt and no gleyed horizon)	Brown calcareous earths	non-alluvial, calcareous loams or clays, no Bt
	Brown calcareous sands	non-alluvial, calcareous sands, no Bt
	Brown calcareous alluvial soils	in recent calcareous alluvium
	Brown earths	non-calcareous, loams or clays, no Bt
	Brown sands	non-calcareous sands
	Brown alluvial soils	in recent non-calcareous alluvium
	Argillic brown earths	in loams and clays with Bt
	Palaeo-argillic brown earths	with palaeo-argillic Bt
Podzolic soils (soils with a podzolic B)	Brown podzolic soils	with Bs and no continuous E
	Humic cryptopodzols	with very dark humose Bhs, no continuous E
	Podzols *(sensu stricto)*	with continuous E and/or Bh or Bhs
	Gley-podzols	as above but with gleyed horizon below B
	Stagnopodzols	with peaty topsoil and/or gleyed E
Surface-water gley soils (soils with humose upper horizons and gleyed in upper part of profile)	Stagnogley soils	with distinct topsoil
	Stagnohumic gley soils	with humose or peaty topsoil
Ground-water gley soils (soils affected by free ground-water)	Alluvial gley soils	with distinct topsoil in clayey alluvium
	Sandy gley soils	sandy, with distinct topsoil, no Bt
	Cambic gley soils	non-alluvial distinct topsoil, clay or loam
	Argillic gley soils	with distinct topsoil and Btg
	Humic-alluvial gley soils	with humose topsoil in clayey alluvium
	Humic-sandy gley soils	with humose topsoil in sands
	Humic gley soils *(sensu stricto)*	non-alluvial, loamy or clayey with humose topsoil
Man-made soils (soils with thick man-made A or disturbed soil)	Man-made humose soils	with thick man-made A (including Plaggen soils)
	Disturbed soils	without thick man-made A
Peat (organic) soils	Raw peat soils	without earthy topsoil
	Earthy peat soils	with earthy topsoil

recognition that soils should be grouped together on the basis of soil characteristics, not environmental conditions. Secondly, time and time again differences in emphasis stem from differences in local conditions. It is not surprising that in Britain stress should be placed on the extent and nature of gleying while in the US soil temperature regimes are given just as much emphasis.

It is obvious, therefore, that soil classification is to some extent a matter of personal suitability. Since so much of the literature uses terminology other than that of the Seventh Approximation—undoubtedly the most comprehensive of the available systems—we have opted to employ terms which are in common use (Table 5.7). Equivalent terms from both the American system and Avery's British scheme (1973) have been included wherever possible. We have adopted this approach despite its imperfections, since we consider it the most suitable alternative available.

Table 5.7   Simplified terminology employed in this book

Class	Major environment of occurrence
Arctic brown soils	Arctic/sub-arctic; well drained sites
Brown soils	Cool and warm temperate deciduous woodlands
Chernozems	Steppe grasslands
Chestnut soils	Semi-arid margins of steppe grasslands
Desert soils	Hot and cold deserts
Ferrallitic soils	Equatorial climates
Ferrisols	Tropical climates; mainly on basic materials
Gleys	Poorly draining sites (bottomlands/clays)
Grey wooded soils	Continental cool temperate woodlands
Lithosols	Recent or eroded unconsolidated materials
Peats	Sites with excessive water supply
Podzols	Cold and cool temperate woodlands and equatorial forest
Prairie soils	Mid-continental grassland/woodland transition
Rendzinas	Limestones
Red and brown Mediterranean soils	Warm temperate (seasonal rainfall) mixed evergreen forest; on calcareous materials
Red-yellow podzolic soils	Warm temperate climates
Regosols	Recently exposed rock surfaces
Sierozems	Desert margins
Solonchak	Mid-continental grassland on alkaline parent materials/ground-water
Tropical ferruginous soils	Tropical climates; mainly on acid materials
Tundra soils	Arctic/sub-Arctic depressions
Vertisols	Tropical and sub-tropical climates; especially in bottomland sites

5.3 Mapping

Convenient as it is to be able to refer to a particular soil by a brief taxonomic term, it is often more helpful to obtain an impression of the spatial pattern of soil variability. The production of soil maps is, therefore, essential, both as an aid to understanding the interrelationships within the landscape and as a means of evaluating soil resources. For example, a soil map may help to establish the nature of the relationship between slope conditions and soil form, which is important in assessing the capability of land for cropping or indicating alternative routes for a highway.

When choosing both the scale of mapping and the type of classification system the requirements of the user are necessarily important. Published soil maps commonly range from *c.* 1:10 000 (6 in. to 1 mile) at the largest, to reconnaissance and atlas maps at as little as 1:80 million (1 in. to 1 250 miles). Relatively few countries have been able to afford the resources to embark on a detailed soil mapping programme, so most countries of the developing world are restricted to the production of reconnaissance maps at 1:250 000 or even smaller. The task has become easier since mappers have been able to use images from the Landsat satellites (*Fig 5.1*). By monitoring radiation from the earth in certain specific, narrow wavebands, it is possible to differentiate areas of, for instance, green vegetation, moist soil and bare soil. Since these and other controls on radiation levels are often closely correlated with soil conditions, it is proving possible in certain circumstances to construct adequate maps based on satellite imagery—albeit at a reconnaissance scale [Westin and Frazee (1976), Townshend (1981)]. However, although boundaries can be delineated by this imagery, we can only establish the actual soil characteristics by ground sampling.

In selecting the scale of the final map one is also determining the size of the smallest area which can be depicted—the Dutch call this the basic mapping unit. Thus, if the smallest area which can be represented is 2 mm x 2 mm on a map, at 1:10 000 this is equivalent to a ground area of 20 m x 20 m. This to some extent establishes the appropriate level of classification. For example, if one is mapping at 1:200 000 (*c.* 1 in. to 3 miles) it would be inappropriate to base the classification on organic matter content because this tends to vary very rapidly. However, a map produced at 1:10 000 (6 in. to 1 mile) would not be very valuable if differentiation was only at Soil Order level (for example, between Spodosols and Alfisols). In fact, it would be quite possible for the whole of the map area to fall into just one of these categories, and the opportunity to identify small areas of difference would have been lost. Having established the scale at which the mapping is to be carried out, it is logical next to consider the classification system to be used.

In mapping, the surveyor's prime interest is in identifying which types of soil are present. A skilled surveyor, with a strong appreciation of the interdependence of landforms, hydrology, vegetation cover and parent

(a)

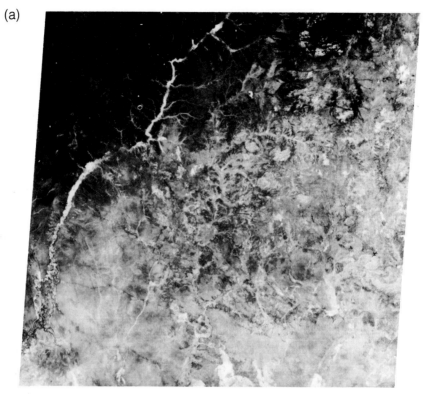

Fig 5.1   (a) *above* A satellite image of part of central Sudan. (b) *opposite* Interpretation allows the
differentiation of dunes, inselbergs and clay plains
[source: National Aeronautics and Space Administration; interpretation according to
Mitchell (1975)]

materials, is often able to make reasonable predictions of the soils likely to be
found. Before going into the field much information on these variables can be
obtained from topographic and geological maps and particularly from aerial
photographs (*Fig 5.2*). On the strength of this it may be possible to construct a
sketch map of the area, on which 'landscape units', where similar soils are
likely to be found, may be identified. Much reconnaissance mapping for land
evaluation purposes is based on these 'landscape' or 'terrain' units [see Mitchell
(1973)].

Before soil survey can be started in earnest it is usual to obtain by field
reconnaissance some idea of the characteristics of the soils and hence of their
variability. This is most rapidly achieved with a screw auger which, although it
destroys the structure, readily yields information on horizon depth, colour and
texture. In this way the units on the sketch map can be characterised more
accurately and areas of intense variation can be recognised.

(b)

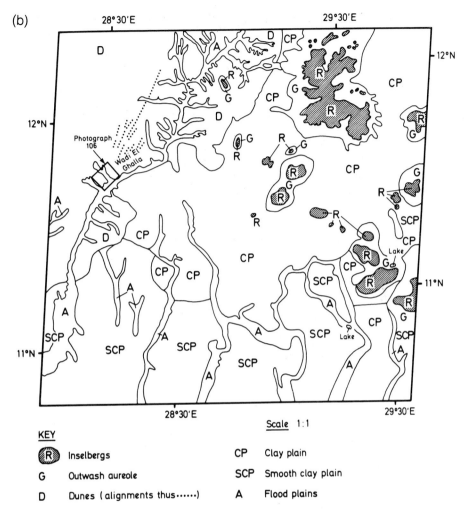

KEY

   (R) Inselbergs

   G   Outwash aureole

   D   Dunes (alignments thus ······)

   CP   Clay plain

   SCP Smooth clay plain

   A   Flood plains

Several common alternative methods of sampling are used to establish the pattern of soil variation and, in particular, the boundaries between units. Where topography and vegetation show little evident variation or where the nature of the landforms is concealed, as, for instance, in close woodland, a system of regular grid sampling may be employed. This has long been the method used to work over large parts of the forested areas of West Africa. On the other hand, if the landscape shows strong contrasts, as where distinct slope facets are clearly visible, it may not be difficult to predict where a pedological boundary occurs. The surveyor may either rely upon this purely interpretative approach or, more often, opt to establish the precise position of the boundary by augering on either side of its estimated position.

Determining boundary locations in this manner assumes that a sharp boundary is readily recognisable. In many cases, perhaps the majority, this is not so. Usually the line shown so firmly on the printed map represents a zone of transition between adjacent soils, although an effort is made to place it in the position of maximum change, however that is defined.

There are problems in defining major boundaries, but they pale somewhat in comparison with the difficulty of deciding how far the separation of small areas of distinct soils should proceed. Unless an extravagant part of one's resources is

Fig 5.2   The complex pattern of soils developed in silty clay material of old river distributaries contrasts with the peaty material of the intervening areas, Chatteris, Cambridgeshire

to be expended on a very detailed survey, mapping units must inevitably contain soils other than those designated in the class name. Thus the Soil Survey of England and Wales claim that their series as mapped contain not more than 15 per cent of other series. However, Bie and Beckett (1971), in a statistical examination of the variability within a series, have suggested that a figure of 50 per cent impurity may be nearer the mark. Concerning the variation in individual properties, Bascomb and Jarvis (1976), analysing the Denchworth mapping unit, found that properties such as the percentage of $CaCO_3$ showed very large variations while the particle sizes were relatively constant. Where the pattern is still more involved it is usual to create mapping units known as **complexes**. The constituent series are usually indicated, but an estimate of the area of land occupied by each is rarely given. Occasionally, in very favourable circumstances, it may be possible to demonstrate the precise nature of a complex soil pattern by reference to aerial photographs (*Fig 5.2*).

Mapping is further assisted by the fact that a soil series very often occupies a characteristic position both within the landscape and in relation to other series. Soil associations, defined in this way, provide a further tier of less detailed mapping, which is useful on smaller-scale maps. The Soil Survey of Scotland have used the association as a mapping unit for many years. It is defined very broadly (viz. soils developed on lithologically similar parent materials), but encompasses certain specified soil series whose characteristics can be spelled out. For example, the Kilmarnock Series (p. 120) always occupies drumlin crests, while the Kilmaurs Series is found in the intervening troughs. They can both be accommodated under the umbrella term 'Kilmarnock Association'. Similarly the soil sequence on Plynlimon (p. 122) of Hiraethog, Manod and Ynys Series can be grouped into the Hiraethog Association. Soil complexes also come under the association umbrella, being treated as components in the same way as series.

Once the boundaries between the mapping units have been identified, the surveyor must dig and describe **modal profiles**, which are taken to be representative of the units in which they have been mapped. To supplement the information obtained by field examination, laboratory analyses are usually carried out on samples from these profiles.

So far we have assumed that the production of soil maps at medium scale (that is, between 1:10 000 (*c.* 6 in. to 1 mile) and 1:100 000 (*c.* ½ in. to 1 mile) is a useful and necessary exercise. What objectives are these maps meant to fulfil? Do they succeed? Clearly, the second question largely depends on the precise nature of the publication. The first can be answered more generally.

Most survey organisations are particularly concerned that their product should be of value to agriculturalists, but obviously only the largest-scale maps will be of interest to individual farmers. Agricultural planners and conservation officers are most likely to use medium-scale soil maps. In developing countries the map provides vital information on which soils are most appropriate to be taken into agriculture or improved, e.g. by drainage or irrigation. In developed countries, where the competition for land is intense, soil maps may provide a good physical basis for deciding which areas should be preserved for agriculture and which should be regarded as negotiable for urban and industrial development. If the criteria used in defining the units are appropriate, medium-scale maps may also be of assistance to engineers, especially road engineers. Clearly the soil map will never replace detailed site investigations, but it may considerably reduce the time spent on preliminary route or site location [see, for example, McGown and Iley (1973)].

Apart from being valuable inventories of a natural resource, soil maps are frequently very useful to a variety of academic investigators. Geomorphologists and geologists often find the detailed information on parent materials which is usually provided on maps of larger scale than 1:100 000 of great value. This is partly because even very thin superficial deposits are pedologically important and are therefore described, although they may be omitted from geological drift maps. The characteristics of the soils themselves may also yield information on, or at least clues to, the sequence of slope development. Archaeologists have long appreciated the dependence of man on the vagaries of his natural habitat. Prehistoric sites are often located on particularly favourable soils, as early cultivators with their primitive tools were only able to till the lightest of soils. Therefore a soil map may provide vital environmental information in tracking down settlement sites.

6 Soil response

6.1 Soil associations

Soil profiles usually show rapid spatial variations in response to the interaction of constantly changing environmental controls. It is a mistake to assume that all, or even most, soils are of what used to be referred to as the 'normal', freely draining or 'zonal' type. It is obviously advisable to consider not isolated profiles but rather soils in relation to one another within a given area. We shall therefore illustrate this discussion by refererence to **geographical associations** of soils. We hope that in this way the variations of hydrology and parent material, along with changes in slope, which interact to produce the pattern of soil distribution, will be more readily appreciated.

It would be impossible to discuss all associations of soils. Accordingly only those groupings which are of wide occurrence or of considerable agricultural importance have been included.

6.2 Soils of the high latitudes

In sub-polar areas—loosely referred to as the tundra (*Fig 6.1*)—permanently frozen ground or *permafrost* dominates soil formation. The position of the permafrost table varies, but over much of the tundra it lies between 20 cm and 2 cm below the surface. Although other factors must be taken into account, it is generally deeper in freely draining gravels than in finer-textured materials. During the summer melt the seasonally thawed layer tends to become waterlogged, even supersaturated, because drainage is impeded by the permafrost. In this condition it is particularly susceptible to movement, or *solifluction*, even on very low-angle slopes. A similar situation often exists in soils of sub-Arctic areas where, although there is no true permafrost, drainage in the upper layer is severely impeded until the whole profile has thawed completely. On level sites *cryoturbation*, or frost heave, is more in evidence than

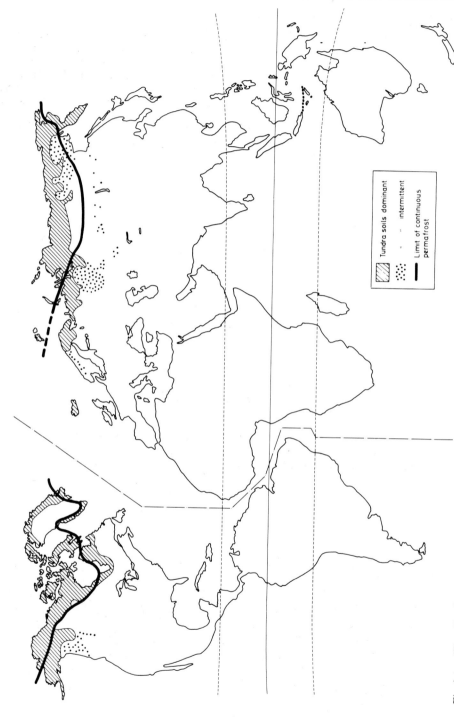

Fig 6.1   The distribution of tundra soils and their relation to the permafrost limit

Plate 1. Ferrallitic soil, near
Abeokuta, South West Nigeria;
typical of freely drained sites in
humid tropical regions where much
of the silica has been removed from
the clay minerals. The mineral
fraction is rich in iron and
aluminium oxides and in residual
quartz.

Plate 2. Chestnut soil, South West Saskatchewan, Canada; in this transition
soil between true Black Earth Chernozems and Desert soils, the Ah
horizon is much suppressed and secondary calcium compounds are
deposited quite close to the surface.

Plate 3. Soil development in the Sub-Arctic is often severely disturbed by solifluction, which in this case has resulted in the overturning of an incipient Podzol.

Plate 4. Acid Brown soil, Central Wales. These freely draining soils are typically developed under acid grassland vegetation in cool humid temperate climates.

Plate 5. Rendzinas, such as this profile on the chalk of the Berkshire Downs, are typically thin, with a sharp contrast between the Ah and C horizons.

Plate 6. Part of a mottled horizon in a Surface Water Gley soil in Southern England. The grey colours due to anaerobic conditions on ped faces and in root channels are readily contrasted with the brown colours within the peds.

Plate 7. Iron Podzol soils, such as this from northern Norway, are
typically found under mor organic matter in freely draining locations.

Plate 8. Humus-iron Podzol developed on a sandy parent material,
Hollandsfjord, north Norway.

solifluction. This is because saturated soil is trapped between the freezing surface layer and the permafrost table. The expansion associated with ice formation subjects this 'sandwich' of unfrozen soil to considerable pressure which can only be relieved if the surface ruptures and material from below is forced upwards, forming disturbances or involutions. Such features are not only evident in high latitudes, they also occur commonly in areas formerly subjected to periglacial conditions, such as southern Britain and the northern United States (*Fig 6.2*). These geomorphic processes therefore frequently suppress the rather feeble pedological development which takes place in sub-Arctic and Arctic zones.

Fig 6.2   An involution in river gravels, Hampstead Marshall, Berkshire

Furthermore, the fact that drainage is restricted by the presence of permafrost, even on quite considerable slopes, partly explains why **gleyed tundra soils**(**Aquepts** in the Seventh Approximation) are by far the most common soils to be found in areas such as the western Canadian Arctic [Tedrow et al (1958)] (*Fig 6.3*).

Although precipitation is low—rarely exceeding 100 mm p.a. in the western Canadian Arctic, for example—evapotranspiration is negligible since low temperatures and high relative humidity often prevail. This compounds the effects of permafrost and explains why saturated, anaerobic conditions are widespread,

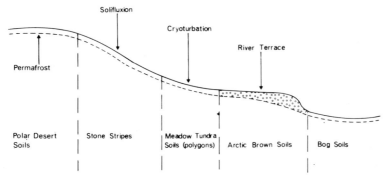

Fig 6.3   Elements of an arctic landscape and associated soils

especially over large areas of rolling 'Arctic meadows' (*Fig 6.4*). Under these conditions gleying is the dominant process in the seasonally thawed layer, while the sparse plant cover decays only slowly in waterlogged conditions and produces a thin accumulation of peat (rarely more than 20 cm) (*Fig 6.5*). However, as in other parts of the tundra, cryoturbation disturbs what would be the 'normal' pedologic horizonation.

Where the terrain is level or depressed, or precipitation greater, waterlogging may persist throughout the summer. In this case effective organic

Fig 6.4   Arctic meadows with steep slopes beyond, Banks Island, Canada. Compare with Fig 6.3

decomposition is minimal and substantial thicknesses of peat accumulate over the permafrost. These are the **bog soils** (**Histosols**), the poorest draining members of this soil assemblage.

At the other extreme, on the exposed, wind-blown plateaux, especially on the polar margins of the tundra, characteristics associated with desert soils are encountered. The resemblance lies in the shallowness of soil development, suggestive of a regosol, the dearth of surface vegetation, and especially the accumulation of carbonates and, less frequently, saline deposits on the undersides of cobbles near the surface. It seems that, however slow it may be, there must be an upward movement of salts in solution in response to the low vapour pressure of the atmosphere, creating the distinctive properties of these **polar desert soils** (**Orthids**) [Claridge and Campbell (1968)].

In freely draining but less exposed positions profiles display certain very weak affinities with podzolic soils. These are the **arctic brown soils** [Tedrow and Hill (1955)]. They are restricted, occurring only where the permafrost is deep and drainage is relatively free (sands and gravels of terrace benches, eskers etc.). In

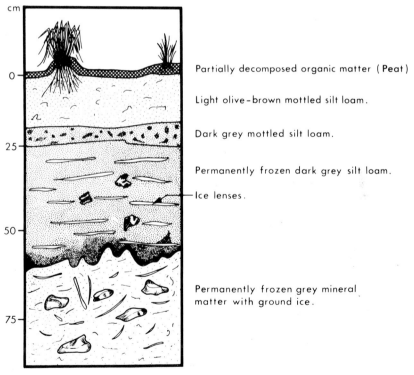

Fig 6.5   A tundra gley soil of the Arctic meadows
[source: Tedrow *et al.* (1958)]

Fig 6.6   An arctic brown soil, Devon Island, Northwestern Territories, Canada. The dark-coloured Bw horizon overlies the paler parent materials

these conditions little disturbance is caused by cryoturbation or solifluction because of the freer drainage. These circumstances do not often occur, and these soils should not be regarded as 'typical' of tundra environments. In general, an ABwC profile can be recognised (*Fig 6.6*) in which a shallow, organic-rich A horizon overlies a brown (hue: 7.5YR) mineral horizon. This normally develops on a coarse-textured parent material. For example:

Vegetation: *Carex*, *Dryas*, *Salix* and mosses
Drainage: free

Horizon	*Depth* in.	
A	0–2	brown (7.5YR 4/2) gravelly loamy sand, loose and friable
Bw1	2–10	brown (7.5YR 5/4) gravelly loamy sand, loose and friable
Bw2	10–18	pinkish-grey (7.5YR 6/2) gravelly loamy sand, loose and friable
C	18–24	light grey sand with 'salt and pepper' effect, loose

[source: Tedrow and Douglas (1964)]

Of particular pedogenic interest is the B horizon which derives its colour from ferric oxides liberated during weathering. In some soils the percentage of Fe_2O_3 remains constant throughout the profile, indicating the low leaching potential of the soil. Elsewhere, especially at lower latitudes, there is a clear increase in the percentage of Fe_2O_3 with depth, suggesting that some translocation of iron is taking place. Nevertheless, the dominant process seems to be weathering *in situ*, which produces, according to the nature of the parent material, profiles similar to the sols bruns acides and brown calcareous soils (Ochrepts) of more temperate climates.

Because of cryoturbation many of these soils are juxtaposed in a very intricate way. For instance, many gently sloping areas have a strong development of polygons (*Fig 6.7*) and the considerable microrelief gives elevated central areas which are comparatively dry (**upland tundra soils**) whereas the low portions are commonly covered with water (**meadow tundra soils**). A similar complex pattern of tundra soils develops on slopes where stone stripes, solifluction lobes and oval soil ridges produce a very irregular surface which becomes more pronounced as the slope steepens.

Fig 6.7   Polygonal ground in northern Canada. Each of the polygons is about 30 m across

It can be seen that several factors bear on the soil hydrology, which is itself the critical influence on soil formation. It not only controls the extent to which translocation can take place, but also influences solifluction and cryoturbation. Conditions in the high latitudes result in an association of soils showing little profile development but responding to the varying conditions of drainage and soil disturbance (Plate 3).

6.3   Soils of the cool and cold temperate climates

Moving away from the polar areas, where there are practically no trees, we come to the zone of coniferous forest. Coniferous associations are generally found where at least one month has a mean monthly temperature of less than 5 °C. Where winters are less severe, as in New England, the Appalachians and the maritime regions of north-western Europe, broad-leaved deciduous trees become dominant. Although there are – or were, before the land was cultivated – considerable areas which could be described simply as coniferous or deciduous forest, it should be appreciated that transition zones (ecotones) are also very extensive. Thus much of central Ontario and southern Quebec carries an association of white pine (*Pinus strobus*) and hemlock (*Tsuga canadenis*), together with birch (*Betula* spp), maple (*Acer* spp) and oak (*Quercus* spp).

These areas of North America and Eurasia, formerly covered by coniferous and deciduous woodland, have been extensively cultivated and have supported rapidly rising industrial populations over the last 150 years. The soils originally developed under the forest cover are therefore of major interest, and will be considered in some detail. The principal soil profiles produced in response to the interactions of various environmental controls will be considered first, as this should enable the association patterns to be more readily understood.

As the intensity of translocation increases calcareous materials are first decalcified, then subjected to lessivage and possibly even podzolisation. On parent materials of glacial or periglacial origin eluviation may have been operating for only 10 000 years or even less (i.e. since the retreat of the Weichselian (Wisconsin) ice sheets). Because they have been forming for a relatively short period, many soils on calcareous tills and similar materials remain only partially decalcified. Elsewhere, where either the parent material is less calcareous, or leaching is more effective, or soil has been forming for longer, lessivage and weathering *in situ* are dominant. But wherever the profile has been markedly acidified, as for instance under pine or heath, lessivage may easily have given way to podzolisation. Thus considerable areas of the Atlantic fringes of Europe, as far south as Cape Finisterre, carry podzolic soils. This, of course, is in addition to northern Canada, Scandinavia and northern Russia where podzolisation is dominant (*Fig 6.8*). However, where drainage is impeded or the water table approaches the surface, gleyed soils occupy much of the area, irrespective of the processes taking place at freely draining sites. It has already been suggested that there may be embryonic podzolisation in the Arctic, but the presence of permafrost at high latitudes effectively restricts drainage over vast

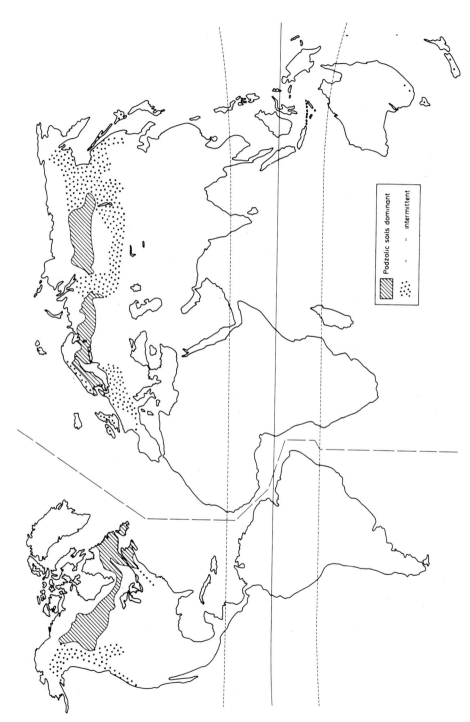

Fig 6.8   The distribution of podzol soils

Podzolic soils dominant

"   "   "   intermittent

areas and confines the Arctic brown soil to just a few locations. South of the permafrost limit (*Fig 6.1*) freely draining sites become much more common and conifers, which can take advantage of the still restricted growing season, are dominant. Conifers provide litter which is resistant to decomposition and create an acidity which inhibits bacterial and earthworm activity. Only the fungi can decompose the litter effectively in these conditions, and the incorporation of organic matter into the mineral soil is also minimised, largely because of the dearth of earthworms. Consequently a mor horizon develops (§ 3.2). Particularly under the climatic conditions of the continental interiors and with strong leaching an **iron**—or Boreal—**podzol (Orthod)** (§ 4.3.4) is produced which can usefully be thought of as the modal podzol. These soils can be recognised by their bleached but shallow Ea (albic) horizon which overlies a deep, orange, non-indurated Bs (spodic) horizon (Plate 7). It is characteristic of these soils that no accumulation of organic matter is visible in the B horizon.

Where leaching is less effective, as in the lowland regions of the British Isles (precipitation *c.* 600–700 mm p.a.), podzols are confined to coarse-textured, base-deficient parent materials such as old river terrace flint gravels. On rather richer materials, such as fine-grained sandstones, there is likely to be only incipient podzolisation. Bleaching of some of the sand grains in the A horizon and a slight enrichment of the B horizon with sesquioxides to give the characteristic rusty colour may be the only visible signs in the field of the onset of the process. Where there has been ploughing even these signs may have been erased. Kubiëna (1953), referred to these transitional soils as **podzolic braunerde** while the Seventh Approximation includes them in the Sub-order **Orthods**.

Where the rainfall is heavy, as in western Scotland, the hills of western Ireland and the northern plateaux (*vidda*) of Norway, the horizons of the modal iron-podzol are accentuated. The Ea horizon is generally deeper because of the more effective translocation and consists almost entirely of residual quartz grains. Iron may accumulate not only as a diffuse Bs horizon but also in the form of an indurated **iron pan** or 'ortstein', the Bfe. Finally, a distinct, dark coloured humic Bh horizon forms immediately above the Bfe. These are the characteristics of the **humus-iron podzol (Humod)** (*Fig 4.6*, Plate 8). Andersen (1979) has suggested that in Denmark some humus-iron podzols are the end-product of the degradation of the sol brun lessivé or **sol brun acide** (see below, p. 113), although it is most unlikely that this is always the case.

The experience of Guillet *et al.* (1975) in the Vosges certainly suggests that a change from high forest to heathland may be instrumental in causing a profile approximating to an iron podzol to change into a strongly cemented humus-iron podzol. This transformation seems to be characterised by the disruption of cutans produced during the first stage and the removal from the profile of the weathering products of the A and E horizons.

Further variants—mainly involving a degree of gleying—are associated with drainage impedance due either to the pan or to the fine texture of the parent material. Where the gleyed features are confined to the Ea horizon and above it can be assumed that water movement has been restricted by the iron pan (ortstein). If this impedance is severe, the decomposition of organic debris will be inhibited and peat may accumulate at the surface (*Fig 4.6*) giving a **peaty podzol** (**Aquod**).

However, not everyone agrees that such soils result from drainage impedance brought about by the pan. For instance, Proudfoot (1958) has argued that peat development may be also associated with prehistoric cultivation, while Crampton (1963) suggested that changed climatic conditions may be responsible.

When podzolisation occurs in topographic depressions and a water table is close to the surface, gleying may reach a maximum in the lower horizons producing a **gleyed podzol** (**Aquod**).

When organic decay does not yield an adequate supply of chelating agents (§ 4.3.4) and leaching is reduced, podzolisation is replaced by lessivage or by weathering *in situ*. The profiles thus formed display either an ABtC or an ABwC horizon sequence. Just as podzols are often found in areas of coniferous forest or heathland, so brown earths and related soils are frequently found under broad-leaved deciduous woodlands (*Fig 6.9*).

When there is virtually no translocation, whether on acid or calcareous materials, horizons are very unclear, merging imperceptibly into each other (Plate 4). In the **acid brown soil**, however, a cambic Bw horizon can frequently be recognised by its vivid orange colour, caused by the liberation of ferric oxides. This contrasts markedly with the rather soft, even dull tones of the Bw horizon of the **brown calcareous soil**. This generally develops on calcareous deposits with a high proportion of impurities—on the chalk marls (such as the Lower Chalk in England), on loess (as in the Picardy region of the Paris basin and in Flanders), or on calcareous deposits that have undergone solifluction (*Fig 6.10*). The integration of these carbonates into the matrix, coupled with the rather small percentage of iron, produces a creamy brown colour throughout much of the profile.

Where the stabilising influences are not present, weathering still proceeds but is supplemented by lessivage and gives rise to **leached brown soils** (**sols bruns lessivés; Udalfs**).

Many have argued [e.g. Mackney (1961)] that leached brown soils can be regarded as precursors of podzolisation. One occasionally observes profiles in which there is a clear Bt horizon with a strong accumulation of clay, but the Eb horizon contains bleached sand grains or even a very thin, but recognisable, bleached Ea horizon. Such soils are called **podzolic brown earths** (**sols lessivés; Orthods**).

On areas where limestones, such as chalk, form the parent material, especially on steep slopes and where the material contains few impurities, thin, highly calcareous soils frequently develop. These are the **rendzinas**, or **Rendolls** of the Seventh Approximation (*Figs 6.10* and *6.11*).

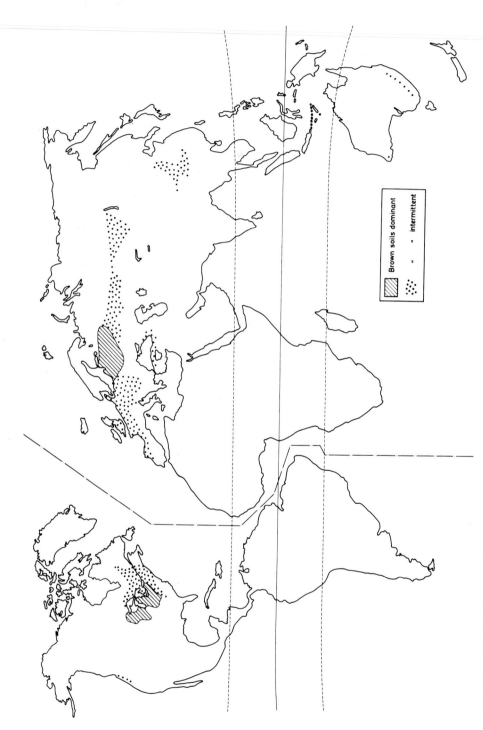

Fig 6.9   The distribution of brown soils

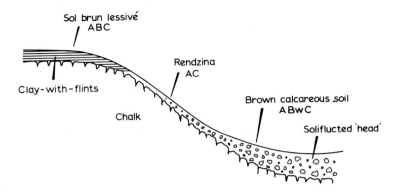

Fig 6.10   The sequence of soils associated with superficial deposits on a chalk escarpment

A high proportion of free carbonates, and hence a high base saturation, in the A horizon is characteristic of these soils. This is often maintained by turbulent creep in the soil mantle, whereby weathered limestone is continually supplied to the solum, effectively counteracting any decalcification. These soils are mostly covered by grassland, in which the fescues (*Festuca* spp) are prominent. With a high level of biotic activity, a very stable calcareous mull forms, giving the A horizon a very dark colour, only interrupted by specks of white carbonate (*Fig 6.11*, Plate 5). The low level of impurities, such as clay minerals, left after

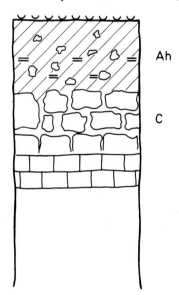

Fig 6.11   A rendzina soil. Here a thin black A horizon rests directly on white chalk rock
            For symbols see p. viii

solution of the limestone, tends to restrict the depth of soil development. In the Middle Chalk of southern England these impurities account for only about 3 per cent of the total mass. On slopes the soil is even shallower because of the continual loss of material by mass movement. The turbulent state of these soils effectively suppresses translocation so that no B horizon is recognisable, i.e. there is an AC profile.

Whereas free drainage is normal in rendzinas, gleyed soils are more typical of areas with impeded drainage. Reduction of iron compounds to the ferrous state usually results from waterlogging which, in turn, can be attributed to one of two main causes: a high ground-water table, or the inability of the soil to cope with the supply of surface water because of low permeability or high effective rainfall. In the first case the grey and blue colours so typical of ferrous compounds are found mainly in the lower horizons, giving a **ground-water gley** (*Fig 6.12a*). In the latter, it is the topsoil which is gleyed, producing a **surface-water gley** or **stragnogley** (*Fig 6.12b*).

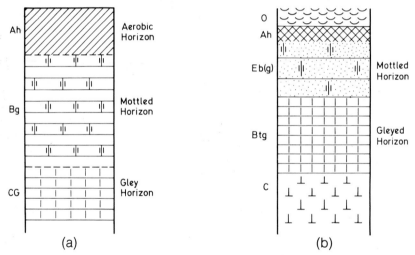

(a)   (b)

Fig 6.12   The profile characteristics of ground-water gley (*left*) and surface-water gley soils (*right*). For symbols see p. viii

As *Fig 6.12* shows, parts of these gleyed profiles normally remain ungleyed, since only those parts of the zones subject to seasonal waterlogging are reduced. Seasonal hydromorphy is commonly seen as a mottled horizon (Plate 6). Here the greys and blues of the ferrous compounds mix with the browns and oranges more typical of oxidised ferric iron.

Although many classifications recognise gleys as one of the principal soil classes the Seventh Approximation does not separate them as an Order. However, they are differentiated within most of the ten Orders. In many ways this is a welcome approach since it removes gleyed soils from the category of 'intrazonal' or extraordinary soils and recognises them clearly as variants which are associated with a wide range of freely draining soils.

Over considerable areas the net supply of moisture is so great that anaerobic conditions prevail almost continuously. As we have seen, plant debris in these

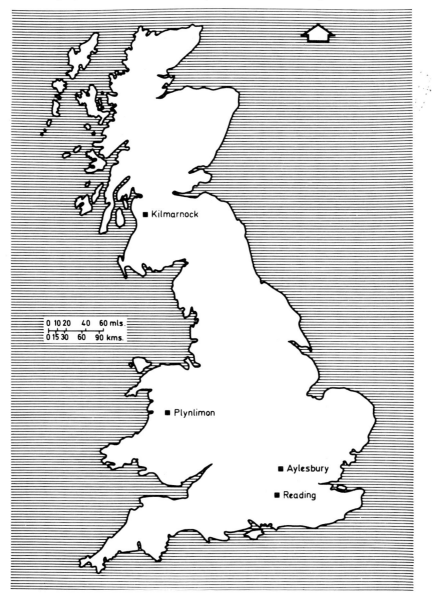

Fig 6.13   The location of the British sites described in the text

circumstances is not subjected to the intense biochemical attack experienced in more freely draining soils because many micro-organisms are unable to survive. It therefore accumulates to form a purely **organic soil** or **peat** (**Histosol**).

These organic soils occur frequently in valley bottoms where high water tables are common and a great deal of water is received from upslope. **Basin peats** or rheophilous mires [Moore and Bellamy (1972)], as these soils are called, may be either acid or alkaline depending on the source of the ground-water or the conditions under which they formed. Thus, for example, the calcareous ground-water derived from the chalk flanking the peats of the Cambridgeshire Fens in East Anglia can give peats on the margins a reaction in the neighbourhood of pH 7–7.5. Generally, lowland peats with a basic reaction are described as **fen peats**. Organic soils can also form on interfluves and even on hill slopes, but here the waterlogged conditions are normally maintained by a high rainfall, aided by a bedrock of low permeability. In parts of North America and Europe, especially along the Atlantic coasts of Newfoundland and the British Isles, heavy precipitation is complemented by a high cloud cover which restricts evaporation. These **hill peats** or **blanket bogs** are usually acidic because of the dissolved CO_2 in the rainwater and the rapid leaching of bases.

Having looked at the principal soils which are found in these areas of cool and cold temperate climates, we can now assess the ways in which the soils are likely to relate to one another in the landscape. We can do this by examining several soil associations from very different parts of the British Isles where there is great variety in climate, landform and lithology—some areas with rainfall in excess of 2000 mm, others where it rarely exceeds 650 mm, areas of acid and calcareous parent materials, of high and low relief (*Fig 6.13*).

6.3.1 The Kilmarnock area, Ayrshire, south-west Scotland

[Soil Survey of Scotland, sheet 22]
Soil development on glacial drift

The basis of mapping in Scotland for a long time has been the association or hydrologic sequence [Glentworth and Dion (1949)] (*Fig 6.14*). All soils

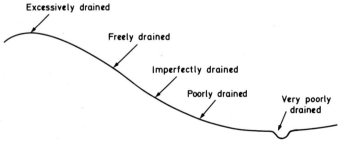

Fig 6.14   The basis of the Soil Association as developed in Scotland

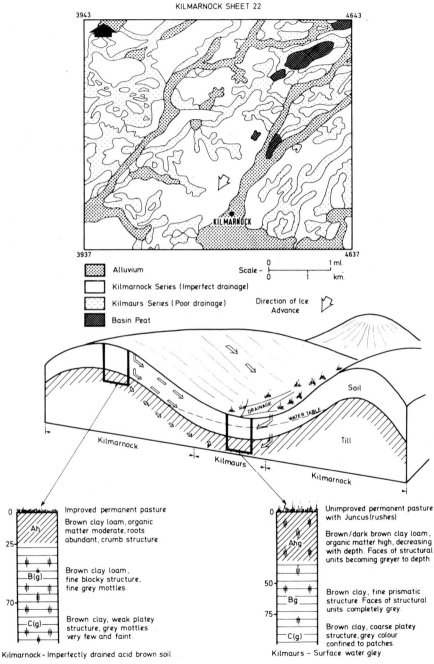

KILMARNOCK SHEET 22

Alluvium

Kilmarnock Series (Imperfect drainage)

Kilmaurs Series (Poor drainage)

Basin Peat

Scale –

Direction of Ice Advance

Soil

Till

Kilmarnock

Kilmaurs

Kilmarnock

DRAINAGE

WATER TABLE

Ah

0

25

Improved permanent pasture

Brown clay loam, organic matter moderate, roots abundant, crumb structure

B(g)

Brown clay loam, fine blocky structure, fine grey mottles.

70

C(g)

Brown clay, weak platey structure, grey mottles very few and faint.

Kilmarnock - Imperfectly drained acid brown soil

Ahg

0

Unimproved permanent pasture with Juncus(rushes)

Brown/dark brown clay loam, organic matter high, decreasing with depth. Faces of structural units becoming greyer to depth.

Bg

50

Brown clay, fine prismatic structure. Faces of structural units completely grey.

75

C(g)

Brown clay, coarse platey structure, grey colour confined to patches.

Kilmaurs - Surface water gley.

Fig 6.15   The area near Kilmarnock, Scotland. The block diagram shows a perspective sketch of part of the drumlin field

developed on the same parent material are grouped together in this unit, irrespective of the drainage conditions of the profile. Freely draining podzolic soils (Spodosols) may be constituent members of the same association as humic gleys (Aquepts). Each of these constituents is shown separately on the map, but their interrelationships are clearly expressed.

This can be seen in the area of lowland around Kilmarnock (*Fig 6.15*), which displays a drumlinoid landscape, created during the last glaciation. The Kilmarnock Association, based on a parent material of till of medium clay texture derived derived from sedimentary rocks and lavas of Carboniferous age, is widely distributed in this area. Rainfall varies between 900 mm and 1200 mm per year, the higher rainfall occurring on the uplands to the east. The components of the Association clearly distinguish between drumlin crests, the steep slope and the troughs (swales), mainly by variations in soil drainage. The drainage is most free on the drumlins themselves with the swales acting as receiving sites for run-off. Even so, in the west, the crests are only imperfectly drained, mainly because of the high clay content of the soil, and drainage in the troughs is poor. At higher elevations (to the east) the greater effective rainfall means that even the soils on the ridges show severe mottling typical of poor drainage. Not surprisingly, then, conditions in the troughs are wet enough to give a peaty surface horizon.

Thus, on the more freely draining drumlin mounds where weathering releases much iron to stabilise the aggregates, the Kilmarnock Series—an acid brown soil (Ochrept) with some mottling in the Bw horizon—is dominant. The inter-drumlin swales are usually occupied by the Kilmaurs Series—a non-calcareous gley (Aquept) which is maintained in a state of near-saturation by the water draining from the adjacent slopes. Drainage problems are enhanced by the low permeability of the profile itself. It is therefore a surface-water gley or, after Avery (1973), a stagnogley. As there is little evidence of translocation, weathering and gleying being the main processes, the Kilmaurs Series falls into the order Inceptisols in the Seventh Approximation.

Generalised profile descriptions:

Kilmarnock Series
(brown forest soil of low base status—equivalent to an acid brown soil; Ochrept)
Slope: gentle
Aspect: east
Altitude: 150 ft (47 m)
Vegetation: Poa trivialis (rough-stalked meadow grass), *Lolium perenne* (rye grass),
        Ranunculus spp. (buttercups), *Trifolium repens* (white clover)
Drainage class: imperfect

Horizon	Depth in. (cm)	
Ah(g)	0–10 (0–25)	brown (10YR 5/3) loam to clay loam; medium crumb, friable; organic matter moderate, roots abundant; few faint mottles along root channels in upper 2 in. (5 cm); *sharp change to*
Bw₁g	10–22 (25–55)	brown (7.5YR 5/1) clay loam; fine sub-angular blocky, firm; organic matter low, roots frequent; few fine mottles; *merging to*
Bw₂g	22–28 (55–70)	brown (7.5YR 5/4) clay loam; weak medium to coarse sub-angular blocky; grey mottles faint; *merging to*
Cg	28–40 (70–100)	brown (7.5YR 5/4) clay loam; weakly laminated, slightly indurated; roots rare; grey mottles faint

[source: Mitchell and Jarvis (1956)]

Kilmaurs Series
(non-calcareous surface-water gley; Aquept)

Slope: very gentle
Aspect: south-west
Altitude: 250 ft (75 m)
Vegetation: Agrostis tenuis (common bent-grass), *Trifolium repens* (white clover), *Juncus effusus* (soft rush), *Ranunculus repens* (buttercup), *Poa trivialis* (rough-stalked meadow grass)
Drainage class: poor

Horizon	Depth in. (cm)	
Apg	0–9 (0–23)	brown to dark brown (10YR 4/3) clay loam; sub-angular blocky, faces of peds greyish; *moderately sharp change to*
Ahg	9–16 (23–40)	yellow-brown (10YR 5/4) clay loam to clay; ill-defined prismatic structure; few faint mottles; *sharp change to*
A₂g	16–20 (40–50)	light yellow-brown (10YR 6/4) clay loam to clay; weak prismatic structure; many coarse distinct grey mottles, faces of peds completely grey; *sharp change to*
Bg	20–29 (50–75)	brown to dark brown (10YR 4/3) clay loam to clay; fine medium prismatic structure; faces of peds completely grey, gleyed; *merging to*
C(g)	29–38 (75–100)	brown to dark brown (10YR 4/3) clay loam to clay; few fine faint ochreous mottles

[source: Mitchell and Jarvis (1956)]

Note: a decrease in mottles to C(g) shows this to be a surface-water gley

6.3.2   The Plynlimon area, central Wales

An illustration of the impact of slope processes and slope hydrology on soil formation

Many of the areas now subject to cool temperate climates were once exposed to glacial or periglacial conditions, sometimes as recently as 10 000 years ago, and so the pattern of soils does not necessarily closely reflect that of the solid geology. In the Plynlimon region of Powys in central Wales, remnants of a till deposit are preserved in the valley bottoms while on hillslopes periglacial activity has produced a thick mantle of angular shale fragments commonly up to 15 cm long. Similar deposits are found in similar topographic positions and the soils largely reflect the distribution of these deposits.

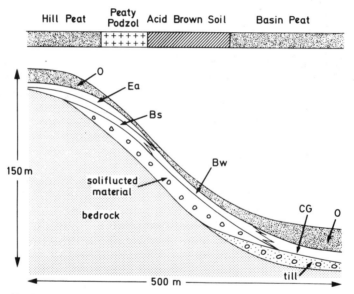

Fig 6.16   A generalised hillside section, Plynlimon, central Wales

Fig 6.16 shows a generalised section of a hillside at between 450 and 600 m above sea level. On the flat interfluve, which according to Brown (1960) is a remnant of a Tertiary erosion surface, a rainfall of about 2000 mm is not easily disposed of by surface run-off, and so a hill peat has developed (*Fig 3.7*). As slopes steepen to *c.* 11° moisture is more easily removed and the peat thins rapidly to be replaced by a peaty podzol (Aquod) of the Hiraethog Series (*Fig 6.17*). Lack of faunal activity has resulted in what is virtually a total separation of the deep mor type of organic accumulation from the mineral soil. The dearth of fibrous roots and polysaccharide gums in the upper mineral horizons restricts the formation of constructional aggregates, and the structure is

Fig 6.17   A peaty podzol soil. The bleached Ea horizon can be clearly seen. It overlies the Bs horizon while the darker grey tone at the surface is the peaty O horizon

characteristically blocky or prismatic. Although the weathering of the shales produces a high silt and clay content, drainage is relatively efficient and translocation has produced strongly podzolised features. On the steepest sections of the slope (up to *c.* 17°) the podzol gives way to an acid brown soil (Ochrept) of the Manod Series, which may represent immature profile development on unstable material. Buried profiles created by soil instability on these steep slopes are common, while on the lower slopes the basal horizons become progressively more gleyed as the water table comes nearer the surface. Finally, in the valley bottoms, the drainage is further restricted by the massive heavy clay of the residual till. Vertical water movement is impeded so much that a valley peat, often over 1 m thick, or, at the very least, a peaty gley (Ynys Series) mantles the gentle slopes adjacent to the streams.

This association of soils, dependent on both hillslope hydrology and the nature of the periglacial processes, can be picked out on the soil map (*Fig 6.18*). Similar associations are to be found on a variety of parent materials in both the northern Appalachians and the Hercynian massifs of western Europe.

Generalised profile descriptions:

Hiraethog Series
(peaty podzol; Aquod)
Slope: 12°

Aspect: south-east
Altitude: 420 m
Vegetation: Nardus stricta (mat-grass), *Molinia caerulea* (purple moor grass)
Parent material: solifluincluded shales
Drainage: free unless iron pan is continuous

Horizon	Depth cm	
O	15–0	7.5YR 2/1 very dark brown organic matter; *sharp junction with*
Ea	0–5	light grey silty clay; prismatic structure, *sharp junction with*
Bfe	5–5.5	intermittent, but sometimes continuous, iron pan, soft and plastic when wet
Bs	5.5–6.8	ochre/red silty clay becoming lighter and with more shale fragments at depth; prismatic structure (size as above); *merging to*
BsC	6.8–80+	finely fractured shale with clay in interstices

Manod Series
(acid brown soil; Ochrept)
Slope: 15°
Aspect: south-east
Altitude: 360 m
Vegetation: Nardus stricta (mat-grass); Ericaceae; *Agrostis tenuis* (common bent-grass)
Parent material: solifluincluded shales
Drainage class: free

Horizon	Depth cm	
O	10–0	7.5YR 2/1, very dark brown organic horizon; *sharp junction to*
A	0–8	brown silty clay with weak blocky structure; *merging to*
Bw	8–28	dark ochre silty clay with shale fragments; weak blocky structure; *merging to*
BC	28–50+	ochre shale with clay in interstices

Ynys Series
(deep peaty gley or peat; Aquept or Histosol)
Slope: 5°
Aspect: south-east
Altitude: 305 m
Vegetation: Juncus effusus (soft rush), *Sphagnum* spp, *Polytrichum commune* (starwort)
Parent material: till derived from Silurian shales
Drainage class: very poor

Horizon	Depth cm	
C	45–0	dark red-brown peat;
CG	0–140+	grey clay with some sub-rounded shale pebbles; massive structure

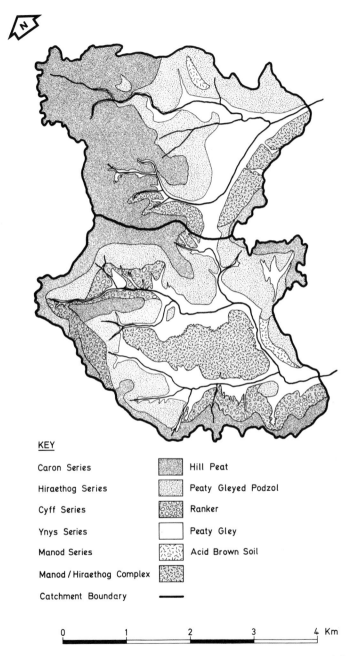

KEY

Caron Series		Hill Peat
Hiraethog Series		Peaty Gleyed Podzol
Cyff Series		Ranker
Ynys Series		Peaty Gley
Manod Series		Acid Brown Soil
Manod / Hiraethog Complex		
Catchment Boundary		

0   1   2   3   4 Km

Fig 6.18   The distribution of soils on the headwater catchment of the river Severn and the river Wye, Plynlimon

6.3.3   The Aylesbury area, Buckinghamshire, south-east England
[Avery (1964)]
The importance of superficial deposits in soil formation

This area includes parts of the Cretaceous escarpment (the Chilterns) of
south-east England. The solid rock, although variable in character, is chalk. To
the north-west lie sandstones and clays which have been eroded to produce a
low-lying vale. The variable lithologies of the chalk provide a variety of parent
materials, and superficial deposits derived in large measure from the chalk also
create strong contrasts.

It is these superficial deposits, rather than drainage, which are dominant in
determining the soil pattern. Loveday (1962) has recognised three distinct
types. Dominating the crests is the 'Plateau Drift' which consists of a matrix of
clay and silt with occasional inclusions of sand. Set in this are a variety of
pebbles, mainly flint from the chalk, but also some far-travelled material.
Plateau Drift can be several metres thick but thins rapidly with increasing slope
(*Fig 6.19*). It is often found resting on a much thinner tenacious clay band with

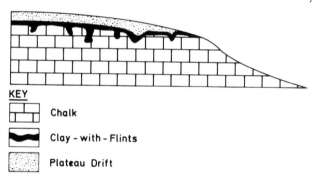

KEY

Chalk

Clay - with - Flints

Plateau Drift

Fig 6.19   The relationship between solid chalk and superficial deposits on the Chiltern Hills

flints called 'Clay-with-Flints'. This deposit is rarely more than 2 m thick. On
the lower parts of the scarp slopes a solifluacted material called 'chalk head' is
found. It comprises chalk rubble set in a fine matrix, often containing
admixtures of Clay-with-Flints and Plateau Drift, which have been sludged from
upslope. Because of the presence of chalk rubble this is an alkaline parent
material, in marked contrast to the other superficial deposits which gave
moderately acid reactions.

With such variations in the parent materials the soil distribution is not as
dependent on drainage as in the Kilmarnock area. However, because of the
derivation of the materials, the soil series occupy characteristic topographic
positions (*Fig 6.20*). For example, on interfluves on the dip slope where chalk is
capped with Plateau Drift and Clay-with-Flints a leached brown soil with gleying
is dominant:

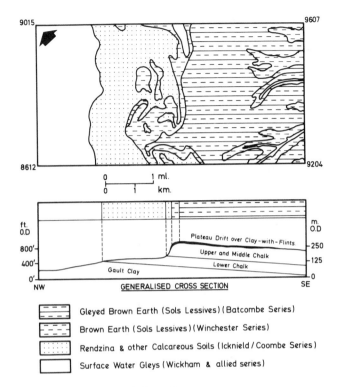

Fig 6.20   Soils of the Chiltern escarpment and clay vale

Batcombe Series
(leached brown soil (gleyed); Udalf; developed on Plateau Drift)
Slope: 1°
Altitude: 775 ft (250 m)
Land use: woodland
Vegetation: Fagetum rubosum (beech) and *Quercus robur* (oak); *Ilex aquifolium* (holly)

Horizon	Depth in. (cm)	
L	2–1 (5–2)	litter, mainly beech leaves;
FH	1–0 (2–0)	mainly partially decomposed leaves, traces of humus;
A	0–1.5 (0–4)	dark grey (10YR 3/1) friable silt loam; weak crumb structure; *clear irregular boundary with*
Eb	1.5–9 (4–23)	yellow-brown (10YR 5/6) friable silt loam; occasional small flints; very weak crumb structure; *sharp irregular boundary with*

EbBt	9–16 (23–40)	strong brown (7.5YR 5/6) friable silty clay loam, finely mottled with redder colours; small flints more numerous, fine sub-angular blocky structures, some having pale coloured silty coatings; *sharp undulating boundary with*
B₁tg	16–29 (40–75)	strong brown (7.5YR 5/6) firm flinty silty clay to clay, faintly mottled; moderate medium blocky structure, aggregate faces smooth, shiny and pale; common small rounded manganiferous concretions;
B₂tgCg	29–90+ (75–230+)	yellow-red, very firm flinty clay predominantly mottled with broken and nodular flints; blocky structure

[source: Avery (1964)]

This soil is gleyed at the base because of imperfect drainage associated with the heavy clay of the parent material and the almost level sites on the interfluves between the dry valleys. Acid conditions restrict stable structure formation and allow lessivage to produce a textural contrast between the Eb and Bt horizons. This in turn emphasises the gleying of the Bt horizons.

Where the slopes steepen away from the escarpment crest the Plateau Drift thins out and the underlying Clay-with-Flints is revealed. The steeper slope allows better water disposal and this is reflected in the ungleyed profile described below. This example helps to show the variety of profiles that are covered by the term 'leached brown soils' and to indicate why they are grouped as separate soil series.

Winchester Series
(leached brown soil; Udalf; developed on Clay-with-Flints)
Slope: 6-7°
Aspect: south-west
Altitude: 750 ft (230 m)
Land use: woodland
Vegetation: Fagus sylvatica (beech) in closed canopy

Horizon	Depth in. (cm)	
L	0.5–0 (1–0)	litter, mainly beech leaves, thin and discontinuous powdery humus layer;
A	0–2.5 (0–6)	very dark grey-brown (10YR 3/2), very flinty friable loam; *irregular boundary with*
Eb	2.5–7 (6–18)	brown (10YR 4/4), very flinty friable loam with weak structure; *sharp smooth boundary with*
Bt	7–15 (18–40)	yellow-red, very flinty, very firm clay with brown structural faces and many black specks; flints large; medium to coarse blocky structure;
BtC	15–24 (40–60)	disturbed chalk with patches of reddish-yellow chalky loam and yellowish-red clay containing unbroken flints;

| C | 24+
(60+) | fissured brown-stained chalk *in situ*, with nodular flints and inclusions of reddish clay |

[source: Avery (1964)]

On the steeper slopes below the outcrop of the Clay-with-Flints, solifluction has been active and creep is still important. The chalk is continually being disturbed and incorporated into the moving mantle. Not surprisingly, the soils are thin and highly calcareous. When, as is common, they develop under grassland they are particularly rich in fauna, especially earthworms, which encourage the formation of a calcareous mull. They therefore approximate to the classic rendzina (Rendoll) profile.

Icknield Series
(rendzina; Rendoll; developed on chalk)
Slope: c. 20°
Aspect: west
Altitude: 675 ft (220 m)
Vegetation: chalk grassland, i.e. *Zerna erecta* (upright brome grass), *Festuca ovina* (sheep's fescue)

Horizon	Depth in. (cm)	
A	0–7 (0–18)	dark brown (7.5YR 3/2), friable humose loam containing chalk lumps; strong granular to fine sub-angular blocky structure; *clear smooth boundary with*
AC	7–13 (18–33)	brown-stained chalk brash with a matrix of brown, friable, more or less humose, chalky loam;
C	13–50+ (33–120+)	fissured and fragmented white chalk

[source: Avery (1964)]

Note: these soils are only of restricted extent, occurring mainly where steep slopes prevail.

At the foot of the escarpment solifluction and creep material have accumulated from upslope. This is of mixed derivation, containing both Plateau Drift and Clay-with-Flints, but the dominant contribution is of the chalky rubble which gives this 'head' deposit an alkaline reaction. This material has accumulated over a long period, but most of the movement must be ascribed to the Weichselian cold period when the area was subject to periglacial conditions. Buried soils are commonly found within the deposits, but the basic contemporary profile is an ABwC form of brown calcareous (Ochrept) type—the Coombe Series.

Coombe Series
(brown calcareous soil; Ochrept; developed on chalk head)
Slope: 1–2°
Aspect: west
Altitude: 625 ft (200 m)
Land use: beech woodland
Vegetation: Fagus sylvatica (beech) and *Hedera helix* (ivy)

Horizon	Depth in. (cm)	
L	0.5–0 (1–0)	litter of beech leaves;
A	0–6 (0–15)	very dark grey (10YR 3/1) friable silty clay loam containing fragmented chalk; strong granular to fine sub-angular blocky structure; *sharp boundary with*
Bw	6–11 (15–25)	brown (10YR 5/3–5/4) friable silty clay loam containing fragmented chalk and small shattered flints; strong fine sub-angular blocky structure; *sharp irregular boundary with*
C	11–24+ (25–60+)	very pale brown (10YR 7/4) chalky silty clay loam containing numerous sub-rounded chalk fragments and few shattered flints

[source: Avery (1964)]

There is a major contrast between the base of the scarp slope, with its freely draining brown calcareous soils, and the almost level sites of the clay vales where the parent material weathers to a fine-textured soil. This, along with a high natural water table, makes for slow drainage. The soils are often calcareous because of the addition of material from the scarp slope by creep or solifluction.

Wicken Series
(surface-water gley; Aquept; developed on Gault Clay)
Slope: 2°
Aspect: south-east
Altitude: 290 ft (90 m)
Land use: grass-clover ley

Horizon	Depth in. (cm)	
Ap	0–5 (0–13)	very dark grey (5YR 3/1), very firm clay; cloddy structure; *clear irregular boundary with*
Bwg	5–16 (13–40)	olive (5YR 4/3), very firm clay with olive-grey cleavage faces; moderate to coarse prismatic and blocky structure; *clear smooth boundary with*
Cgca	16–30+ (40–75+)	light grey (5YR 7/2) very firm stoneless calcareous clay with yellowish-brown mottling; coarse prismatic structure; secondary carbonate deposits

[source: Avery (1964)]

6.3.4 The Reading area, Berkshire, south-east England

[Soil Survey of England and Wales, sheet 268]
Soil development on a flight of river terraces

The Thames and Kennet valleys in south-east England contain some well-preserved terrace remnants. The terraces vary in age, height and composition so that a sequence of soils varying in response to these controls has formed on them.

The map extract (*Fig 6.21*) shows a typical sequence. Older, higher remnants, mainly consisting of flint gravels, occupy the crest of the interfluve between the rivers Kennet and Pang to the north. They have been subject to soil-forming processes for a considerable time, perhaps about half a million years, so that many of the fines have been lost from the upper horizons producing sharp textural contrasts within the profiles. A humus iron podzol or Orthod (Southampton Series) is widely developed on deposits of the Winter Hill stage and on the higher terraces.

Southampton Series
(humus iron podzol; Orthod)
Slope: level
Altitude: 330 ft (110 m)
Vegetation: plantation of *Pinus sylvestris* (Scots pine) with *Vaccinium myrtillus* (bilberry)
Parent material: flint gravels of fluvial origin on high level terrace

Horizon	Depth in. (cm)	
LF	5–3 (13–8)	dark red-brown (5YR 3/2), loose, well-decomposed humus; *narrow sharp boundary with*
H	3–0 (8–0)	red brown (5YR 4/3), more compacted humus with large pine roots; *sharp boundary with*
Ea	0–6 (0–15)	white (10YR 8/1) sandy gravel; *narrow irregular boundary with*
Bh	6–7 (15–17)	very dark grey (10YR 3/1) humose sandy gravel; *sharp irregular boundary with*
Bfe	at 7 (17)	thin hard discontinuous iron pan; *sharp irregular boundary with*
Bs	7–36 (17–90)	brown (7.5YR 5/4) very stony, firm sandy loam; structureless;
C	36+ (90+)	pale yellow (2.5Y 7/4) sandy loam gravel; very stony

[source: Jarvis (1968)]

Lower terrace remnants and areas incorporating material derived from higher level terraces carry soils which have not developed to such an extent. The soils may be acid and with a low cation exchange capacity but generally the clays

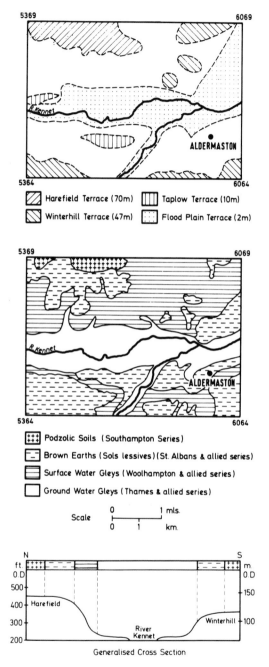

Fig 6.21   Soils of the Kennet valley, Berkshire

have not broken down. Leached brown soils of the St Albans Series are, therefore, widespread on these terraces. At higher levels they may grade into the Southampton Series.

St Albans Series

(leached brown soil; Udalf)

Slope: 1°

Altitude: 325 ft (100 m)

Parent material: flint river terrace sands and gravels

Land use: arable

Horizon	Depth in. (cm)	
Ap	0–7 (0–17)	dark greyish-brown (10YR 4/2), very pebbly, friable sandy loam with weak blocky structure; frequent roots; *sharp boundary with*
Eb	7–15 (17–37)	brown (10YR–7.5YR 5/4), very pebbly, very friable sub-angular blocky structure; few roots; *merging boundary with*
EbBt	15–30 (37–74)	yellowish-red (5YR 5/8), very friable, very pebbly, structureless, loamy coarse sand; *merging irregular boundary with*
Bt	30–35 (74–87)	yellowish-red (5YR 4/8–5/8), very pebbly, structureless, coarse sandy clay loam; sand grains bound by clay coatings;
BtC	35+ (87+)	similar material becoming looser and less compact with depth

[based on Jarvis (1968)]

In contrast with the well-drained terraces, a fine-textured calcareous ground-water gley (Aquent) (Thames Series) is found on the present flood plain. Only on these very recent deposits is the calcareous nature of the catchment seen to affect the soils; elsewhere the materials have been totally decalcified. On the flood plain drainage is very impeded and flooding has, until recently, been common. Largely because of the high levels of organic colloid, the cation exchange capacity is very high (over 65 m.e./100 g) in the surface horizons. On these poorly draining low-lying areas the land is almost entirely under permanent pasture.

Thames Series

(calcareous ground-water gley; Aquent)

Slope: level

Altitude: 135 ft (40 m)

Land use: permanent pasture

Parent material: silt loams of alluvial origin

Horizon	Depth in. (cm)	
Ah₁(g)	0–4 (0–10)	very dark brown (10YR 2/2), stoneless, calcareous, humose, firm clay loam to silty clay with faint yellow mottles; strong, fine crumb structure; abundant fine fibrous roots; *sharp junction to*
Ah₂(g)	4–8 (10–20)	dark grey-brown (2.5Y 4/2) stoneless calcareous clay with many faint olive-yellow mottles and some grey mottles along root channels; sub-angular blocky structure;
B₁g	8–12 (20–30)	light brown-grey (2.5Y 6/2), stoneless, highly calcareous firm silt clay loam with many mottles; blocky structure; *narrow boundary with*
B₂g	12–18 (30–45)	light brownish-grey (2.5Y 6/2), stoneless, highly calcareous, firm silty clay loam; many very faint mottles; structure tending to prismatic; *merging boundary with*
B₃g	18–25 (45–65)	light olive-grey (5Y 6/2), stoneless, highly calcareous, firm silty clay loam with many distinct mottles; moderate prismatic structure; *narrow boundary with*
Cg	25+ (65+)	grey-brown (2.5Y 5/2) intermingled with light yellow-brown (2.5Y 6/4); grey colours along root channels; stoneless, highly calcareous, silty clay loam to silt loam; massive structure

[source: Jarvis (1968)]

Even within a small area such as the British Isles the interaction of environmental controls—climate, vegetation and slope—on the many and varied parent materials results in a pattern of soils showing marked contrasts. A more detailed study of the variation in soil conditions throughout the British Isles is provided by Curtis *et al.* (1976).

6.4 Soils of the mid-latitude grasslands

Away from the coastal margins of North America, Eurasia and South America the effective precipitation (i.e. total precipitation less evapotranspiration) declines rapidly. In the northern continents much of the winter precipitation falls as snow on to land which is already frozen, so that on sites with normal drainage the moisture available for leaching is much reduced compared with the areas discussed in the previous section. However, on lower slopes leaching may still be quite effective because of the water received from the upper parts of the slope.

The effect of the decline in precipitation is well illustrated in North America as one crosses from Lake Superior to the Rocky Mountains. Considering only the freely draining soils–most of which are developed on calcareous tills–a clear sequence can be recognised (*Fig 6.22*).

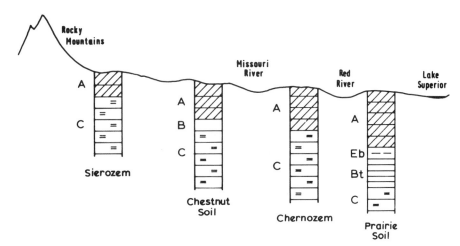

Fig 6.22   A generalised soil traverse of the interior lowlands of northern USA. For symbols see p. viii

The leached brown soils (Udalfs) of northern Minnesota give way westwards to the **prairie soils (brunizems; Udolls)**. These have deep chernozemic (mollic) horizons overlying a Bt horizon in which there are weak accumulations of translocated clay. These soils are generally partially base unsaturated (*c.* pH 6), although the C horizon is often calcareous.

Moving west again into North Dakota or south-western Manitoba one encounters a transition to the AC or ABwC profiles of the **chernozem (Boroll/Ustoll)** belt. These soils display the classic deep Ah horizon, characteristic of grassland soils, in which organic and mineral material is intimately mixed. The colloids are generally dominated by exchangeable Ca^{2+} (*Fig 6.23*), although the profile is depleted of free $CaCO_3$, except in the C horizon. Prairie grasses, particularly the rough fescue (*Festuca scabrella*), have been the dominant vegetation here for a considerable period. These grasses with their dense root systems are extremely effective in recycling the bases and minimising their loss downwards through the soil profile. Anyway, leaching is only modest because of the low effective rainfall. The supply of available calcium is therefore derived in the short term from the litter rather than from the parent material.

Further west, the chernozems give way to soils characterised by even less leaching in which, if the parent material is particularly carbonate-rich, free carbonates may be encountered in the Bw horizon of the ABwC profile. These are the so-called **chestnut soils**, included within the **Xerolls, Borolls** and **Ustolls** by the US Department of Agriculture, in the dark brown soils by the Canadians, and in the kastanozems by the World Soil Classification (FAO). They occupy an extensive area of the North American grasslands (*Fig 6.24*)—an area covering south-eastern Alberta and south-western Saskatechewan as well as most of the Dakotas, and stretching southwards into Nebraska, Kansas and Oklahoma. Chestnut soils have also developed over a vast belt of the semi-arid Russian steppes.

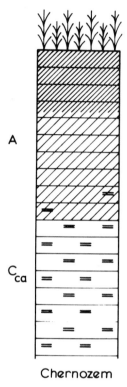

Chernozem

Fig 6.23   The characteristics of a chernozem profile. For symbols see p. viii

On the high plains adjacent to the Rocky Mountains, as the rainfall declines the lusher prairie grasses are replaced by bunch grasses (*Stipa* spp) and even by sage brush (*Artemisia tridentata*). There is a marked decline in organic matter content compared with the soils to the east and again free carbonates are found in the lower part of the solum. Such soils, commonly classified as **sierozems** (**Aridisols**), are of little agricultural value.

The principal consequences of the decline in effective rainfall are:

● a decline in the thickness and organic content of the calcareous mull, or mollic, Ah horizon
● the increasing dominance of calcium on the exchange complex
● a decline in the extent to which free carbonates are translocated

Fig 6.24 shows that chestnut soils are one of the most extensive groups in North

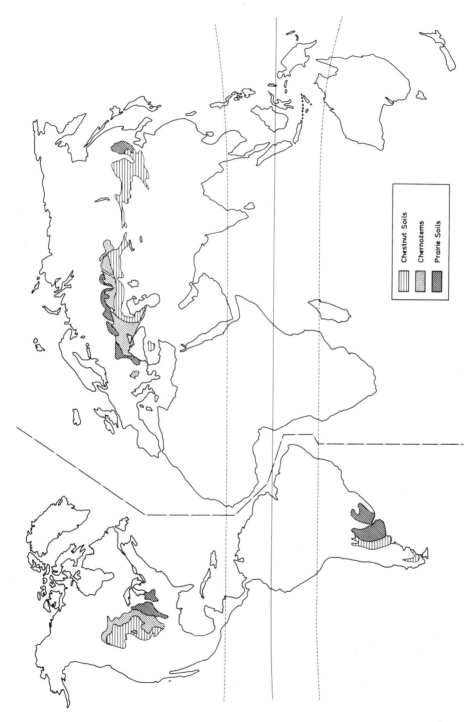

Fig 6.24   The distribution of grassland soils

America and Eurasia. We will therefore look more closely at them and their associated soils by examining the distribution and characteristics of the soils on the rolling Missouri Coteau Upland of southern Saskatchewan (Willow Bunch Lake, map area 72H, Saskatchewan Institute of Pedology) (*Fig 6.25*). The parent material in this area is glacial till derived from calcareous Upper Cretaceous shales. However, other parent materials give rise to similar soil associations. For instance, loessic deposits are commonly found in the chestnut soil zone of both the USA and the USSR.

Fig 6.25   Part of a gently rolling till plain, southern Saskatchewan, Canada

The area has [Ellis *et al.* (1967)] a cool, semi-arid, continental climate with a wide range of *c.* 35 °C (60 °F) between summer and winter mean monthly temperatures. 70 per cent of the precipitation of *c.* 400 mm (15 in.) arrives in convectional rainstorms during the summer months, and 25 per cent is accounted for by winter snow. The combination of high summer temperatures and summer rainfall is critical in understanding the soil moisture regime. This rainfall can only have a superficial effect on the leaching process since much of it is rapidly lost from the soil through evapotranspiration.

Under demanding climatic conditions such as these, the native vegetation in freely draining localities is of short and medium-height grasses dominated by the short-awned porcupine grass (*Stipa spartea*) and wheat grass (*Agropyron* spp). Over-grazing in the early years of the century led to the replacement of many of these native grasses by sagebrush (*Artimisia tridentata*) which provides little protection against erosion and is tough and unpalatable. In contrast, in the wet sloughs, grasses, sedges, rushes and other moisture-loving plants occur.

As we have seen in the Kilmarnock area of Scotland, hydrological conditions are likely to vary considerably on rolling till plains. The disposal of surface water is particularly critical in Saskatchewan, where much of the precipitation is in the form of torrential summer downpours of such intensity that the infiltration capacity of soils on the upper, steeper slopes is often exceeded. As a result much of the water moves down to the gentler, lower slopes where more is able to infiltrate. The leaching process is therefore accentuated here compared with upslope. The nature of the relief is very confused so that surface channel drainage is poorly developed and a high water table is complemented by water accumulating in the depressions or sloughs.

Apart from these low-lying areas drainage is free, and once again we meet with a hydrological sequence of soils (*Fig 6.26*). However, downward movement of water is both sporadic and of limited extent, because of the intermittent nature of the rainfall. Translocation of carbonates in these soils is restricted in extent. Decalcification generally occurs in both the Ah and Bw horizons, but reprecipitation of $CaCO_3$ may be encountered in the Cca horizon where secondary deposits may be seen in the pores. Such soils encountered in mid-slope positions are referred to by the Canadians as orthic dark brown soils and may be equated with variants of the chestnut soils (Plate 2).

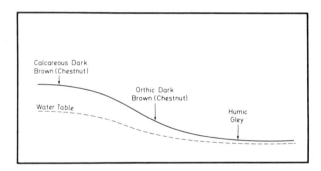

Fig 6.26   The soil association characteristic of undulating topography in southern Saskatchewan

The Amulet Association
(found extensively on the rolling till plains of southern Saskatchewan with the orthic dark brown chernozemic soil (Boroll) occurring in mid-slope positions)

Parent material: fine-textured calcareous and gypsiferous till
Drainage: free

Horizon	Depth in. (cm)	
Ah	0–6 (0–15)	very dark greyish-brown (10YR 3/2), moderate granular clay loam; pH 7.4

Bw	6–17 (15–42)	dark brown (10YR 3/3) to dark yellowish-brown (10YR 3/4), moderate prismatic clay loam; pH 6.4
Cca	17–29 (42–75)	greyish-brown (2.5Y 4/2), moderate prismatic clay loam with high secondary carbonate content; pH 7.4
C	29+ (75+)	greyish brown (2.5Y 4/2), massive clay loam with high percentage of carbonates; pH 7.6

[source: Ellis *et al.* (1967)]

On the interfluval ridges where leaching is less pronounced than downslope, with only the Ah horizon decalcified, secondary carbonates may be evident in both the B and Cca horizons and a calcareous dark brown chernozemic soil (Boroll) forms.

Parent material: fine-textured calcarous and gypsiferous till
Drainage: free

Horizon	Depth in. (cm)	
Ap	0–6 (0–15)	dark brown (10YR 3/3), moderate sub-angular blocky clay loam, low content of free carbonates; pH 7.5
B	6–14 (15–35)	dark greyish-brown (10YR 4/2), weak sub-angular blocky clay loam with high percentage of carbonates; pH 7.8
Cca	14–21 (35–55)	very dark greyish-brown (2.5Y 3/2), massive clay loam with high percentage of secondary carbonates; pH 7.5
C	21+ (55+)	dark greyish-brown (2.5Y 4/2), massive clay loam with high percentage of carbonates; pH 7.9

[based on Ellis *et al.* (1967)]

In contrast with these freely draining profiles the high water table of the sloughs encourages gleying even though this is climatically a semi-arid area. The C horizon, in particular, is strongly gleyed. Furthermore, carbonates are removed from the whole profile except the parent material which generally remains calcareous. These soils are designated as peaty orthic humic gleysols (Aquolls).

Parent material: fine-textured calcareous and gypsiferous till
Drainage: poor

Horizon	Depth in. (cm)	
O	4–0 (12−0)	peaty accumulation; pH 5.6

Ah	0–7	black (10YR 2/1), massive to sub
	(0–18)	6.1
Bw	7–14	black (2.5Y 2/0), massive clay;
	(18–35)	
CG	14+	very dark grey (2.5Y 3/0), massive cla
	(35+)	primary carbonates; pH 7.4

[based on Ellis *et al.* (1967)]

Clearly there are major differences, but the soils of this association also have much in common. We find that the freer draining members have between 2 per cent and 4 per cent organic carbon in the Ah horizon, notably less than in the dark-coloured chernozems to the east. This is because of the much smaller input of organic debris under these more arid conditions. Nevertheless, the organic matter which is produced is rapidly humified and links with the clay and the iron to form very stable structural units. Because of the richness of the grass litter in calcium there is a ready supply of exchangeable Ca^{2+} which encourages the flocculation of this colloidal complex and thus provides the basis for the granular structure of the topsoil. However, this structure is not as strong, nor is the A horizon as darkly pigmented, as in the chernozem. The surface soil may rightly be described as chestnut (Plate 2).

A totally different accumulation is seen in the gley soils of the sloughs. As in the more temperate conditions of southern Scotland, the high water table prevents the decomposition of organic debris, which therefore accumulates at the surface. However, the process is much subdued by the rapid evapotranspiration of the summer months and under these circumstances O horizons rarely exceed 15 cm.

Further differences are apparent if the B horizons are examined. While the calcareous soil of the upper slopes possesses a Bw horizon, which can be attributed to the presence of free carbonates and a colloidal complex dominated by calcium, the orthic dark brown (chestnut) profiles of the lower slopes are totally decalcified and may even show some evidence of incipient lessivage. Weakly developed cutans have sometimes been described, although the precise process responsible for their formation in this environment has yet to be established. However, in all the freely draining soils, weathering *in situ* and calcification play the major roles in soil formation. These processes may also be at work in the gley soils, but here it is gleying which is most evident, producing the blues and greys typical of the CG horizon.

Ploughing and overgrazing of the freely draining chestnut soils have made them especially susceptible to erosion. Removal of the protective vegetation mat for arable cultivation or by overgrazing, combined with intensive summer storms, resulted in the gullying of vast areas of the Dakotas during the 1920s and 30s. Moreover, rainfall in the chestnut soil zone is notoriously erratic, and there can be prolonged periods of drought, during which A horizons depleted of organic bonding agents (originally provided from the decomposition of the fibrous root systems of grassland plants) are likely to fall ready victims to wind erosion. Soils of the chestnut group suffered particularly severely during the drought years of the 1930s. So bad was the devastation that parts of Kansas, Oklahoma and Colorado were called the Dust Bowl [Worster (1979)]. These soils have provided problems for soil conservationists, which have been largely resolved by returning most of them—especially those in the more arid parts—to range farming with stocking at low densities, thus ensuring a permanent and continuous vegetation cover. But erosion damage is not easily rectified, and many of the soils on knolls and ridges in the Willow Bunch Lake area have been so depleted that they are now classed as **regosols**, i.e. soils with only a primitive A horizon lying directly on the parent material.

Eroded profiles are just one variant on the sequence. If the water table remains below the surface in the depressions, the humic gleys may be replaced by **solonchaks** in which, provided the evaporation rate is high enough, the diagnostic A horizon contains a saline crust and efflorescences. This only happens if:

- the parent material is saline
- the water table is sufficiently near the surface to allow upward movement of saline soil water to reach the surface during the dry season
- the water table is not too high seriously to impede the decay of organic matter, in which case a gleyed soil will form

6.5   Soils of the sub-humid and humid tropics

Under this heading is included a vast range of soils forming under a great variety of climatic regimes. Within 5° of the Equator the climate is essentially one of consistently high temperatures and high rainfall. Thus Georgetown (Guyana) records a mean temperature of 30 °C (mean annual range 1 °C) and a rainfall of about 2 250 mm p.a. North and south of this equatorial belt are large areas with contrasting wet and dry seasons, for example Ibadan (Nigeria) with a mean temperature of 25 °C and an annual rainfall of 1 254 mm, most of which falls between April and July and between September and October. Adjacent to this, but still within the tropics, are the sub-humid and semi-arid areas associated with a savanna vegetation where the annual temperature range is markedly greater. For example, Timbuktu (Mali) couples a mean temperature of 30 °C with a range of 13 °C and an annual rainfall of only 230 mm (nearly all of which falls in July and August).

With these climatic differences and the contrasting geological formations, there is a wide variation in the rate and depth of bedrock disintegration. In the humid tropics, for example, where chemical weathering is more rapid than the mass movement of material on slopes, vast depths of *in situ* weathered material may be encountered—up to 100 m in flat localties [Thomas (1966)] and even 30–40 cm on slopes of 60° [Birot (1968) p. 73]. However, in parts of the sub-humid savanna lands weathering accumulations are commonly much less deep.

Both the depth of weathered material and the extent of weathering and leaching are extremely variable. Indeed, many of the systems of soil classification in common use in the tropics make their principal differentiations on the basis of the composition of the weathering residues and the extent of translocation.

Because there is so much variation in the environmental controls and therefore in the soils themselves within the tropics, we shall look at soil formation in both the savanna and forest zones.

6.5.1 Soils forming under sub-humid conditions (savanna and semi-deciduous forest)

In sub-humid regions, and especially in the savanna areas, one often finds landscapes of subdued relief with long, low slopes. Elsewhere extensive and almost level plains or pediments may be separated by steep escarpments (*Fig 6.27*). These landscapes are in marked contrast to the deeply dissected terrain which often, though by no means always, typifies areas of evergreen forest.

In Africa especially, these 'terrain assemblages' recur with almost monotonous regularity. Soil-forming and geomorphic processes, as one might expect, also produce a recurring pattern of parent materials and soils. In recognition of this, an association of soils in which the component members appear in the same topographic relation to one another is called a **catena** [Milne (1935)] (*Fig 6.28*).

When studying soil formation in northern Europe and over much of North America one tends to consider soils principally in terms of the pedogenic processes of weathering and translocation. After all, large parts of these areas have only been free of ice for about 10 000 years, so there has been little opportunity for slope recession since soil formation began. However, in the tropics weathering and translocation have been uninterrupted for several million years, and during this time there has been ample opportunity for lateral eluviation of soil constituents. Furthermore, slope recession involving colluvial and alluvial processes has been in progress throughout the life of the soil, so that these processes are also likely to have had a profound effect on the nature of the soil profiles.

Fig. 6.27   An inselberg and pediment landscape near Bauchi, northern Nigeria

Many different catenas are encountered in the sub-humid tropics, if only because of differences in the underlying geology and geomorphic history. However, since very large areas, especially in Africa, consist of ancient shield rocks—the 'basement complex' of igneous and metamorphic rocks—we will

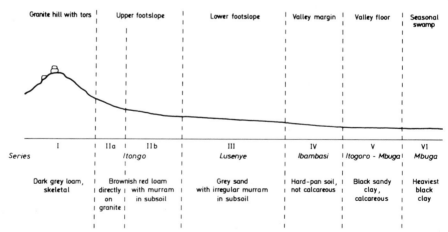

Fig 6.28   An example of a catena – the Ukiriguru catena from Tanzania – as proposed by Milne (1947)

look at a catena developed on fine-grained gneisses and granite, the Iwo Association. This occurs extensively in the forest/savanna transition zone of western Nigeria (*Fig 6.29*).

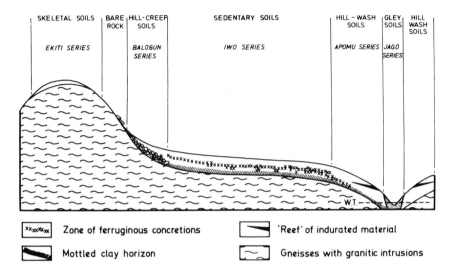

Fig 6.29   The Iwo catena, western Nigeria

Being subject each year to two seasons of heavy rainfall (April to May, and September to October), these soils display both substantial weathering and translocation of material. However, the onset of the dry season causes dehydration of the iron oxides, hence the red colours which are such a striking feature of these soils. Rubefication (§ 4.2.2) is thus a prominent agent of soil formation. Weathering and leaching are intense enough to remove any alkali salts and alkali earths, and to release iron oxides from the primary minerals. As these minerals break down there is some differential removal of silica but much remains to combine with alumina, forming 1:1 clay minerals of the kaolinite family, which, with the iron oxides, remain close to the seat of weathering. Despite this apparently intense alteration, considerable reserves of weatherable minerals remain in the form of rock fragments. A textural B horizon commonly occurs and the presence of clay cutans shows this to be the result, at least in part, of eluviation from the A horizon.

Most of the soils in the Iwo Association can be described as **tropical ferruginous soils** (**Ustalfs**, sub-order of **Alfisols**), but there are other processes operating which enable us to make important differentiations within the catena. In particular, colluvial movements undoubtedly influence the nature of the parent material and are so important a factor that the Soil Survey of Western Nigeria makes use of the term **hill creep soils** for those formed on coarse scree and rubble at the foot of rocky hills (e.g. Balogun Series). Further downslope the parent materials are much finer as a result of the accumulation of material brought from upslope by overland flow (hill wash). Apomu Series are the principal **hill-wash soils** in the Iwo Association. In the region between these

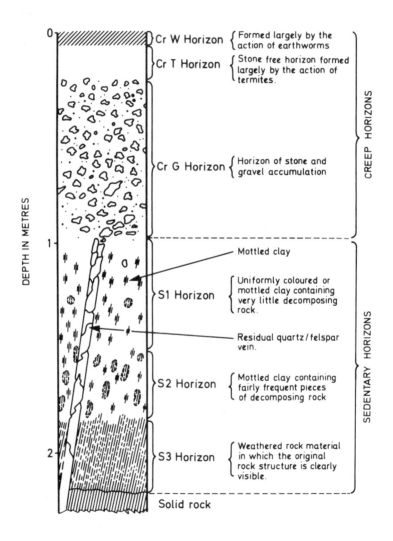

Fig 6.30 Characteristic horizons of a tropical ferruginous soil
[source: Smyth and Montgomery (1962)]

two the soils form directly from the bedrock and can therefore be described as **sedentary soils**. Finally, in the valley bottoms on recent alluvial sediments soils best described as **alluvial soils** are found.

Virtually all the profiles also show signs of colluvial and other movements in their upper horizons, so much so that the morphology due to rubefication is often difficult to recognise. For this reason Nye (1954) argued that the conventional horizon designations A, B, C, etc. were inappropriate for many tropical soils and suggested that two major horizons should be distinguished: (*Fig 6.30*):

- the horizon of soil creep (Cr)
- the sedentary horizon (S)

Nye further subdivided the creep horizon into a layer which is largely the result of worm casting (CrW) and one which appears to consist entirely of material capable of being redistributed by termites (CrT). Below these, at depths of between 25 and 50 cm, it is common to find a horizon rich in quartz and concretionary gravel (CrG). This is most likely to be material left after the fines have been selectively redistributed by animals.

It is often difficult for those who live in temperate latitudes to appreciate the importance of termites and other animals in tropical soil formation. It is worth considering how they operate. Certain species of termite construct nests which reach 2 m or even 3 m in height and may contain 2–3 tonnes of soil (*Fig 6.31*) obtained by burrowing, usually in the topmost metre of the soil. When abandoned, the mounds soon collapse and the material is dispersed by rain splash and overland flow. In a detailed analysis of mounds near Ibadan, Nye (1955) found that the termites with which he was concerned (*Macrotermes nigeriensis*) rarely carry particles larger than 2 mm. Since the gravel-free horizon shows a very similar mechanical composition to that of the mounds, Nye concluded that termites are probably instrumental in producing the CrT horizon. However, there is clearly an element of circular argument here. A conservative estimate of the amount of soil material brought to the surface is about 0.2 tonnes per hectare per annum, or an accretion of about 25 cm in 10 000 years. Watson (1975) found that not only do termites mechanically sort the upper horizons, but their mounds are generally richer in extractable bases than the adjacent soils, especially in zones of low rainfall. He was of the opinion that the source of this enhanced base status was the vegetation carried into the mounds by the termites and differential leaching between mound and surrounding soil.

Earthworms also are often responsible for a great deal of sorting of the surface layers, even more than in temperate areas. Substantial surface casts, frequently in the

(a)

(b)

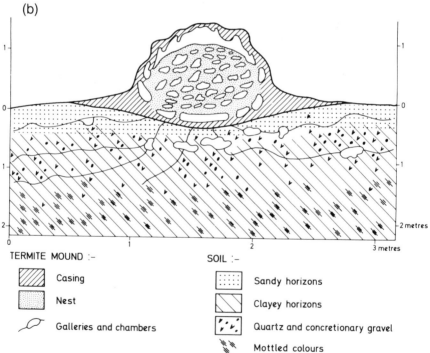

TERMITE MOUND :–   SOIL :–

▨	Casing	
⬚	Nest	
⬡	Galleries and chambers	

⬚	Sandy horizons
◰	Clayey horizons
◰	Quartz and concretionary gravel
※	Mottled colours

Fig 6.31   (a) a termitarium, Nigeria (b) a typical cross-section of a termitarium constructed by
Macrotermes spp
[based on Nye (1955)]

Fig 6.32   Earthworm casts on the soil surface, Ife, Nigeria

form of hollow tubes (*Fig 6.32*) are a common sight on many of these ferruginous soils during the dry season. Since the casts consist entirely of ingested material, the upper particle size limit is less than that found in the CrT layer, rarely exceeding 0.5 mm.

In all the freely draining members of the Iwo Association—the Balogun, Iwo and Apomu Series—the CrW, CrT and CrG horizons can easily be identified. Other horizons can also be recognised. There is a clear textural discontinuity (at about 50 cm in the Iwo Series), caused partly by clay/iron translocation. This is apparent from the cutans which are clearly visible in thin section. Where the parent materials are sedentary a horizon of red and white mottled kaolinite-rich clays (the so-called 'corned beef' horizon) is often encountered below the textural horizon. This mottling is quite distinct from that associated with gleying, the colours being much brighter than in hydromorphic soils. It seems [Vine (1949)] that this horizon is the principal zone of kaolin formation, but the reasons for the mottling are somewhat obscure. It may be inherited from the bedrock, the red zones (often still displaying foliation) being produced from iron-rich minerals such as biotite, and the paler areas representing decomposed feldspars. On the other hand, some migration of the iron compounds may be involved, either as a result of chelation or as ferrous compounds during the wet season when this clay-rich horizon may be waterlogged. This mottled horizon may provide a clue to the origin of the very common pisolitic concretions of iron oxide, whose concentration by termites has been noted above. In 1949 Vine noticed a progressive change from the red parts of the mottled clay to the concretionary gravel above. Smyth and Montgomery (1962) have argued that the concretions are caused by a concentration of iron oxides by deposition either about a nucleus or possibly in the larger pores of the subsoil.

The Balogun Series is typified by the following profile:

Balogun Series
(tropical ferruginous soil; Ustalf)
Slope: steep
Vegetation: rain-forest
Parent material: coarse-grained granitic gneisses
Drainage class: very free

Horizon	Depth in. (cm)	
CrW	0–2 (0–5)	dark greyish-brown, loose, humic, slightly silty clayey fine sand; weak crumb structure; *narrow boundary with*
CrT	2–10 (5–25)	greyish-brown to brown, loose to friable clayey sand with some quartz gravel; structureless; *merging boundary with*
CrG	10–20 (25–50)	brown, friable coarse sandy clay; some quartz gravel and a few feldspar fragments; structureless; *merging boundary with*
S₁	20–50 (50–125)	slightly reddish-brown friable coarse sandy clay; few quartz gravel and feldspar fragments but more pieces of weathered rock; structureless; *merging boundary with*
S₂	50+ (125+)	similar to above but an increasing content of weathered rock fragments and occasional rotting boulders. Fresh rock within 96 in. (240 cm)

[based on Smyth and Montgomery (1962)]

On more level sites the Iwo Series is found whose profile is typified by:

Iwo Series
(tropical ferruginous soil; Ustalf)
Slope: level or gently sloping
Vegetation: derived savanna
Parent material: coarse-grained granite gneiss
Drainage class: free

Horizon	Depth in. (cm)	
CrW	0–2 (0–5)	dark brownish-grey, humic, friable clayey sand; structureless; *narrow boundary with*
CrT	2–10 (5–25)	greyish-brown, friable, clayey sand with some fine quartz gravel and some concretions; structureless; *merging boundary with*
CrG	10–30 (25–75)	orange-brown, friable, very clayey coarse sand; frequent quartz gravel and stones and hard round concretions; structureless; *merging boundary with*
S₁	30–48 (75–120)	orange-brown, friable, coarse sandy clay with some quartz gravel and concretions; a few feldspar fragments; structureless; *merging boundary with*
S₂	48–72 (120–180)	orange-brown, slightly mottled, reddish-brown, coarse sandy clay with some quartz gravel and feldspar fragments and pieces of rotten granitic rock; structureless; *merging boundary with*
S₃	72+ (180+)	increasing content of feldspar and rotten rock until fresh rock is reached at about 96 in. (240 cm)

[based on Smyth and Montgomery (1962)]

Finally, the valley bottoms are mainly occupied by poorly draining soils of the Jago Series. Just as in temperate latitudes, in the tropics ground-water gleys occupy these low-lying sites:

Jago Series
(ground-water gley; Aquent)
Slope: level, valley bottom site
Vegetation: gallery rain-forest
Parent material: alluvium of clayey sand texture
Drainage class: free above water table; overall poor

Horizon	Depth in. (cm)	
Ah	0–2 (0–5)	dark brownish-grey, loose, humic silty fine sand; structureless; *merging boundary with*
Eb	2–10 (5–25)	pale greyish-brown, loose, slightly clayey sand; structureless; *merging boundary with*
Bg	10–30 (25–75)	pale greyish-brown to pale yellowish-brown; loose clayey sand; faint orange-brown and pale grey mottles; structureless; *merging boundary with*
CG	30+ (75+)	pale brownish-grey with variable texture; intensely mottled

[based on Smyth and Montgomery (1962)]

Although sequences of the type just discussed are widespread throughout the savanna and the forest margin, there are often extensive outcrops of ironstone sheets which are probably related to soil formation. Again distinctive catenas can be identified, although not all workers are agreed on the origins of the indurated material. In much of central Nigeria, for example, the ironstone characteristically occurs as sheets or cappings on plateau surfaces (*Fig 6.33*) with virtually no other soil development. At the 'breakaway' margin of the plateaux evidence of active scarp recession is provided by the scree of ironstone boulders which act as the parent material for poorly developed lithosols.

Fig 6.33   Soil development in an area of extensive ironstone cappings in central Nigeria

Away from the retreating escarpment, the Nupe sandstone provides the material for very deep, red soils which are difficult to classify but show certain properties (such as a textural B horizon), which are similar to the ferruginous soils of the Iwo Association.

Widespread speculation about the way the ironstone crusts were formed has produced several alternative explanations. One, which has received some support, suggests that the initial concentration of iron takes place in subsoils on a landscape which displays only low relief (*Fig 4.11*). Much of the necessary migration of iron compounds occurs within the zone of ground-water fluctuation, producing an indurated clay or **plinthite**. Subsequent dissection leaves the water table at a lower position within the soil profile and exposes the plinthite at the surface where, no longer subject to saturated conditions, it hardens to form ultimately massive ironstone sheets. Young (1976), amongst others, has disputed the effectiveness of this transformation, although there is field evidence to support it. So indurated is this ironstone that it forms resistant cappings to the plateau surfaces, protecting them from erosion. With scarp recession, breakaways develop which provide debris for the parent material of creep soils and also for stone lines in the ferruginous soils on the pediments. Where seepage lines exist, iron from this material may be translocated and concentrated as another plinthite layer low down in the landscape, so that the sequence is repeated.

Since mottled plinthite is very common in soils of the forest zone (see below) it is tempting to postulate that climatic change is necessary before irreversible crystallisation of the iron oxides can take place, but there is insufficient evidence for us to be confident about this. However, the whole process of induration and ironstone formation certainly takes place on a geological rather than a pedological time-scale and may date from the Tertiary.

6.5.2   Soils forming under humid conditions (evergreen forest)

Under the heavier effective precipitation experienced in the evergreen rain-forest zone weathering is at work for most, if not all, of the year, and the soluble products are more likely to be removed from the seat of weathering. Accordingly, we need to look at the effects of both vertical and downslope water movements. In § 4.3.7 we discussed the details of ferrallitisation, which is most important in soil formation in this region. Briefly, it involves the total breakdown of the primary silicate minerals into the constituent sesquioxides, silica and bases. The bases invariably are leached away, as is much of the dissolved silica. The sesquioxides, however, are much less mobile and the gibbsite in particular remains largely in place. The amount of clay mineral synthesis depends on the availability of silica. When the parent material is felsic there is an adequate supply of silica and alumina for kaolinite to form in the weathering horizon. On these acid materials, therefore, the profiles may exhibit relatively weak ferrallitisation with goethite and kaolinite dominating. However, on mafic rocks, which are deficient in silica, most of the silica that is dissolved is carried away in solution and, unless it is replenished from elsewhere, there is little clay mineral formation. This allows the fullest development of ferrallitisation, and virtually only the residual oxides of iron and aluminium (goethite and gibbsite) remain.

Clearly, variations in the extent of ferrallitisation are largely dependent on the silica content of the parent material and on the loss or supply of silica by downslope movement. Lévêque (1967) has described a catena on basic igneous rocks in French Guyana which illustrates this relationship well (*Fig 6.34*). On the interfluves the soils now forming are often shallow **skeletal soils** (**Entisols**)

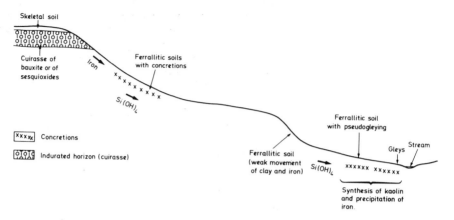

Fig 6.34   A tropical soil catena from French Guiana
[based on Lévêque (1967)]

less than a metre in depth, containing many concretions. However, these are
forming on what must be very substantial palaeosols (duricrusts) in the form of
sesquioxide, even bauxitic, cuirasses which reach a thickness of 20 m in places.
If this interpretation is correct, weathering and translocation may have
progressed for several hundred thousand years at least. Not only are the soils
depleted of silica but one might expect there to have been a considerable
downslope movement of iron oxides. These, presumably under the influence of
organic chelating agents, have produced zones of secondary induration on the
slopes, sometimes as thin cuirasses, but more commonly as concretionary
horizons. Since these concretions are present in large quantities from the
surface downwards, it is possible that there has also been truncation by erosion, a
surmise supported by the lack of CrW or CrT horizons. An example of a soil
profile from such gently-sloping areas is given below:

(strongly ferrallitic soil with yellow over red horizons; Orthox)
Slope: gentle
Vegetation: rain-forest
Parent material: dolerite
Drainage: free

Horizon	Depth cm	
Ah	0–7	brown (2.5-5YR 4/4) changing with depth to reddish-brown (5.0YR 4/8) granular clay loam with fine roots; increasing number of ferruginous concretions; numerous fine roots; *sharp boundary to*
B₁ (kaolin zone)	7–40	bright reddish-brown (5–7.5YR 5/6) blocky clay with numerous concretions and fine roots; *merging to*

B₂ (kaolin zone)	40–105	bright reddish-brown (5YR 5/6) massive clay with large numbers of concretions (up to 5 cm), some of which display traces of bedrock structure; increasing in frequency with depth; several roots; *merging boundary with*
B₃ (kaolin zone)	105–230	bright reddish-brown (5YR 5/6) passing with depth to reddish-brown (2.5YR 5/6) massive clay loam with many concretions (up to 70 per cent by volume) and fragments of bedrock; *merging boundary with*
B₃C	230–270	bright brown (2.5YR 5/6) massive loamy sand with numerous iron/aluminium concretions (less hard than horizon above); *merging boundary with*
C	270+	reddish-brown and red (2.5YR-10R 4/6) massive loamy sand with some small mottles; ferruginised rock fragments at depth with several iron/aluminium concretions

In contrast to this lateral movement of iron from upper to mid-slope regions, there is little evidence of any strong vertical translocation of iron, or indeed of clay, in the mid-slope soils. However, ferrallitisation here is intense with much silica having been lost downslope, leaving a strongly ferrallitic soil dominated by goethite in the parent material and gibbsite in the horizon of maximum clay (Table 6.1).

Table 6.1   Chemical analysis of the clay-sized fraction of a ferrallitic soil

Depth (cm)	Kaolinite (%)	Gibbsite (%)	Goethite (%)	Total (%)
10	25	29	35	89
60	31	44	25	100
350	25	22	49	96

[source: Lévêque (1967)]

In French Guyana these cuirasse-capped plateaux have been deeply incised by the streams which now flow across them, so that steep slopes are encountered on the lower part of the valley traverse. On these relatively young surfaces, soil profile development is restricted to weak translocation of clay and iron, while surface wash removes the topsoil and counteracts any horizon differentiation. Nevertheless, ferrallitisation is intense, and much silica has been lost downslope, leaving clay, gibbsite and goethite as dominant constituents.

On the lower slopes of the catena a clay-rich horizon is encountered above the freely draining parent material. This results partly from the downslope movement of clay, but also from a certain resynthesis of kaolinite due to the greater availability of silica at these lower sites. The soil is highly mottled through temporary waterlogging—hence its designation as a **ferrallitic soil with pseudogleying**.

Finally, in the valley bottoms on alluvial and colluvial sediments there is a series of **gleyed soils** which are influenced by the water table. The downslope movement of clays and iron culminates here, so that the profiles are enriched with translocated clay and iron precipitates out in the vicinity of the oscillating water table. A concretionary horizon usually forms but sometimes soft but substantial cuirasses have been located. For this reason such soils have been called ground-water laterites, although they are true gleys.

It is worth emphasising that the valley bottom soils in this part of Guyana, as in so many other parts of the tropics, are gleyed soils, not the distinctive **Vertisols** or highly expansive black clays (called black cotton soils in East Africa) which are commonly portrayed as occupying alluvial sites. Since Vertisols are characterised by high proportions of montmorillonite—which gives them their capacity for expansion and contraction—they are only likely to form where adequate supplies of silica, Ca^{2+} and Mg^{2+} are available [Kantor and Schwertmann (1974)]. They are most likely to form in poorly draining concavities (dambos) on mafic rocks. Here the silica and bases derived from the breakdown of the rocks upslope can accumulate and montmorillonite can be synthesised. Even then there is no guarantee that Vertisols will form since such soils are by definition self-mulching. For this to take place other conditions must be met. During contraction large cracks form (*Fig 6.35*) into which surface

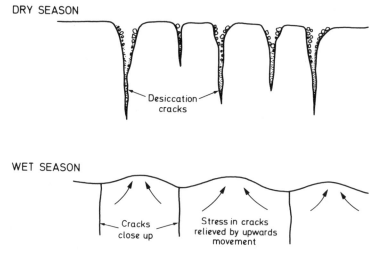

Fig 6.35   The nature of self-mulching mechanisms in Vertisols

material collapses. During expansion the surface heaves to relieve the stress caused by the additional material in the cracks. Clearly, such self-mulching is only possible where there are distinct dry and wet seasons, during which successive contraction and expansion of the clays can take place.

6.6   Time in soil formation

So far we have tried to illustrate how soils are formed without putting much stress on the influence of time. However, it is clear that soils take a long time to develop, certainly hundreds or thousands, and possibly even hundreds of thousands, of years [Gerasimov (1974)]. Therefore we must consider significant past events which may have had an influence on soil formation, particularly variations in climate. It is now well established, for instance, that there have been several cold periods during the Quaternary, separated by periods in which the climate ameliorated to give conditions at least as warm as they are now, and sometimes warmer. During cold periods ice sheets advanced over much of Eurasia and North America, leaving deposits which now mantle the landscape. The duration of soil evolution therefore varies according to the glacial history of the area. In tropical regions, which have not been glaciated, we may be dealing with a period of evolution stretching back into the Tertiary, although we must then take account of the effect of geomorphic processes on the age of the land surface.

Some soils have not had long to evolve, and the inception of some of them can accurately be dated. Consider the soil development of a complex coastal sand dune system, the South Haven peninsula, at the entrance to Poole Harbour, Dorset, England [Wilson (1960)] (*Fig 6.36*). Historical evidence for the growth of the spit complex is available from several maps dating back to 1600. At that time there was only one dune ridge, but in the eighteenth century a spit developed on the seaward side, inhibiting growth of the original dunes. Later still a third ridge was initiated and today there are three fully developed ridges. All the dunes are constructed from the same sand-sized material which is initially calcareous, although most of the material is siliceous. A restricted range of plants has been able to colonise this successfully. Primary colonisation is by salt- and drought-tolerant marram grass (*Ammophila arenaria*), but leaching by rainwater causes rapid desalinisation and decalcification and the sequential colonisation is by acid-tolerant vegetation. The older dune ridges (1 and 2) possess a typical heath assemblage dominated by *Calluna vulgaris* and *Erica cinerea* with isolated *Pinus sylvestris* and *Betula pubescens*.

Profiles taken on the summits of each dune ridge (*Fig 6.36*) reveal that soil development has involved not only desalinisation and decalcification, but continuing and intense acidification, some eluviation, the addition of organic matter to the surface and ultimately the establishment of an incipient iron podzol. The considerable contrasts between the most recent dune system and the older dunes indicate initially rapid changes, with further changes taking place more slowly.

The profiles also show that soil development at the older sites has not taken place without interruption. Buried organic horizons bear witness to the considerable instability of a sand dune area in the early stages of colonisation.

Soils developing on active flood plains show similar evidence of successive sedimentation and sometimes erosion.

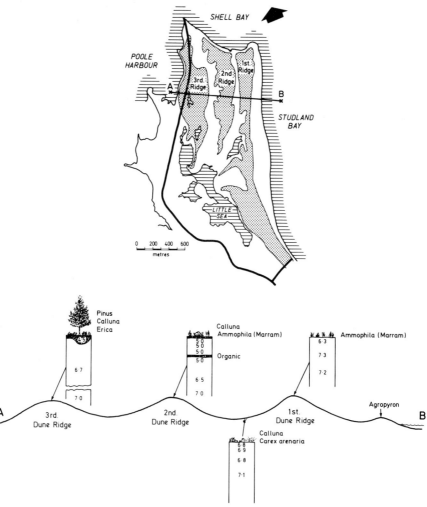

Fig 6.36   Dune systems and related soils, South Haven Peninsula, Dorset. Figures on profiles refer to pH values

The South Haven example gives a glimpse of the early stages of development on a site where there has been no previous soil development and where there are no weatherable minerals or range of particle sizes to encourage a more varied and productive vegetation. Soils on some of the dunes of the Breckland in Norfolk, England, or esker, kame and moraine ridges of northern Europe may have evolved in a similar way.

However, more commonly we are confronted with soils which have been subject to changes in vegetation or climate. Interest centres on the rate at which such soils respond to these changes, and again some idea of this may be obtained from sites with historical records. For instance, over a short time span there are areas which have been reforested with conifers after the removal of a deciduous woodland. Over a longer time span there is evidence from archaeological sites.

The oak woodland of Simon's Copse, Abinger, Surrey, England, was partly cleared and replaced by larch and pine in the 1930s. The area still under oak cover yields a typical profile:

Horizon	Depth cm	
L	1–0	oak leaf litter
Ah	0–45	brown (7.5YR 4/4) sandy loam; large woody roots; large chert fragments at 40–45 cm; very weak granular structure; *gradual transition to*
Bw	45–65	yellowish-brown (10YR 5/6) sandy loam containing yellow and reddish-brown concretions; *gradual transition to*
C	65+	dull yellow-orange (10YR 7/3) sand with numerous chert fragments

Soils which remain under grassland and oak are best described as acid brown soils, showing a very uniform pH profile—6.0 throughout the solum and also in the parent material (*Fig 6.37*). Where conifers have been planted the profiles show signs of differentiation. Thus under pines planted in 1952 the pH of the upper 20 cm has fallen to about 4.0, although the lower horizons remain at 6.0. Apart from this there is little response to the reafforestation. However, where the plantation dates from 1932, bleached grains are very much in evidence in the upper horizons and the acidity of the whole profile has increased to pH 4.0. The forest mull accumulation characteristic of the oak woodland has been replaced by a clearly recognisable mor humus. Everything therefore points to the onset of podzolisation on these sandy soils within only fifty years.

Soil changes on such a short time-scale mainly show up as differences in soil pH and organic matter distributions, e.g. at Abinger and at the South Haven peninsula. More profound developments involving eluviation and weathering show themselves only over longer periods. On both till and solifluction material of the last cold period—say not less than 10 000 years old—profiles showing distinctive horizonation are readily found. Thus, while a few decades see the first primitive changes, 10 000 years seem to be enough for 'mature' development. One of the rare opportunities to trace soil development over the intervening period is by examining profiles buried by the constructions of earlier cultures. Work by Dimbleby (1963) on the buried soils below Bronze

Age burial mounds in Yorkshire and Hampshire has revealed well developed brown soils, in contrast to soils still exposed at the surface which have been severely podzolised. Two conclusions are possible from these observations. One possibility is that the 7000 years between the end of the last cold period and the burial were sufficient only for the development of a mature brown soil profile from the disturbed matrix of periglacial material. Since then development has continued and during the succeeding 3,000 years the brown soils have been

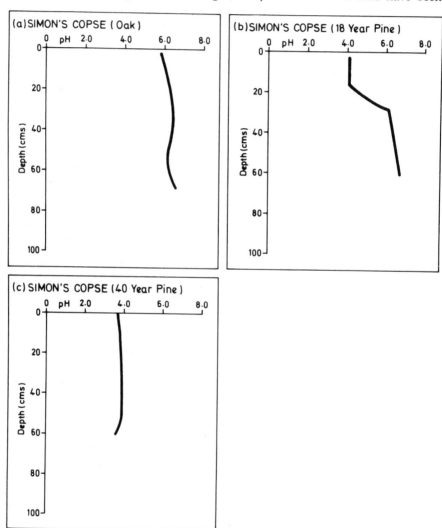

Fig 6.37   pH profiles for soils developed under oak woodland and in recent years subject to coniferous afforestation; Simons Copse, Abinger, Surrey, England

transformed into podzolic forms. Another possible explanation is that when the burial mounds were being constructed, or afterwards, a combination of vegetative and climatic changes took place which caused this major shift to podzolisation. However, as observed above, modification of a developed profile is much more rapid than initial evolution.

Changes in soil morphology with time are not confined to the progressive operation of pedogenic processes. Additions of sedimentary material—often substantial—to already existing soils are well documented in western Europe and North America. We have already seen (p. 126) that the soils of the Chilterns in southern England are closed related to the variety of superficial deposits on which they are developed. However, apparent anomalies which characterise several of the soil series point to a complex sedimentary as well as pedogenic history. The slope areas have been subject to substantial mass movements during the last of the Quaternary cold periods (the Devensian), and on the ridge tops of the interfluval areas we find the Batcombe Series, a leached brown soil, with a clearly defined Ah, Eb, Bt, C(g) profile (p. 127). In this case interest centres on the silt (60–2μm) content, which falls from 58 per cent at the surface to 32 per cent in the Bt horizon and only 6 per cent in the parent material. For the most part the parent material is a clay-rich deposit containing flint clasts, and the large quantities of silt in the upper horizons cannot conceivably have been derived from it.

The dominance of the silt fraction strongly suggests an aeolian origin. Avery and Catt in particular [see, for instance, Catt et al. (1971)], have shown that the mineralogy of the silts in the 'parent material' is very different from that of the silts in the uppermost horizons, thus demonstrating conclusively their differing provenance. Furthermore, Catt has established that these silts show a remarkably consistent mineralogy right across southern England. This all points to an aeolian origin for the material, a possible source area being the outwash plains which occupied what is now the North Sea during the Devensian cold period. Wintle (1981) has recently succeeded in dating some examples of these inorganic sediments by thermoluminescence methods. This independent check has confirmed that the superficial materials sampled were laid down between *c.* 11.8 and 22.4 ka B.P.

It is likely, therefore, that the translocation of clays, and the formation of cutans in the Bt horizon, are partly the result of the climatic amelioration of the last 10 000 years or so. However, the finer texture of the B horizons of these soils may well owe at least as much to the addition of coarse material to the surface as to the translocation of fines to depth.

In this context we should not assume that such additions are confined to regions that have experienced periglacial regimes. It is quite likely, for instance, that the silt and fine sand fraction of many upper horizons of west African soils may be due as much to aeolian additions from the Sahara as to pedogenic processes.

The effects of climatic changes are most readily observed when the soil-forming processes are long-lasting and yield characteristics which are exclusively the province of one climatic regime. For example, several French workers have placed great stress on the significance of red colours in soils of what are now cool temperate climates. Federoff (1966), quoting Boulaine, has gone so far as to suggest that mean annual temperatures must be as high as 16 °C for rubefied clays to form.

The dangers of equating certain soil characteristics with specific climatic conditions are only too evident. For example, many tropical soils show no red colouration at all. This may be due to the parent material but, if so, it shows how necessary it is to avoid generalisations and to relate like to like. Furthermore, Birkeland (1975) has shown that, in some soils of the south-western United States, increasing redness correlates beautifully with increasing age. Whether the two are casually related is debatable. By contrast, John (1980) argues that rubefication in soils of the North Downs, Surrey, 'dates from the more recent stages of the Quaternary'.

Nevertheless, red colours (defined by Avery (1973) as having matrix chromas of greater than 4 in hues redder than 10YR) are rarely found in presently forming British soils, whereas they do occur extensively in palaeosolic horizons [see for instance Sturdy *et al.* (1979)]. Extensive rubefied horizons can be identified on the older terraces of the Thames—e.g. on the Upper Gravel Train of Wooldridge and Linton (1955). Higher up the catchment, in the valley of the river Kennet, a strongly rubefied horizon occurs a metre or so below the present surface on the 47 m terrace. In thin section this horizon is especially striking, with strong separations of intensely reddened illuvial clay unlike anything found in more recent soils [Chartres (1980)]:

Slope: level
Altitude: 125 m
Land use: pasture
Parent material: flint gravels of fluvial origin

Horizon	Depth cm	
Eb	0–25	dark brown (10YR 4/3) stony sandy loam; friable with fine granular structure, becoming weak blocky with depth; *gradual smooth boundary with*
Bt	25–38	strong brown (7.5YR 5/6) very stony loam; weakly developed fine to subangular blocky structure with evidence of cutans; *gradual smooth boundary with*
Eb	38–60	yellowish-brown (10YR 5/4) gravel with a sandy silt matrix; very weakly developed structure; *abrupt wavy boundary with*
Bt	60–160	yellowish-red (5YR 5/6) to reddish-brown at base 5YR 4/4 gravel with sandy clay matrix; very compact sub-angular blocky structure between stones containing strongly developed cutans; black manganiferous staining towards the top of the horizon; *gradual smooth boundary with*

(the Eb and Bt at 38–160 are bracketed together as palaeosol)

C   160–300   strong brown (7.5YR 5/6) flint gravel with sandy clay matrix;
                      distinct horizontal alignment of stones; some fine distinct
                      mottles

Whether or not this and similar profiles can be explained by a warmer, seasonally moist palaeoclimate or by sheer antiquity remains to be resolved.

Clearly the periods of climatic change have to be fairly long-lasting to have any significant effect on the long-term evolution of soils. The eluviation of clays is often very slow but, apart from disruption by cryoturbation or similar processes, irreversible. On the other hand, changes related to the mobilisation of the more soluble constituents may be recognisable after just a few years. The speed of development is largely a function of the rate and amount of water movement and the buffering capacity of the soil. Hence soils with sandy textures are probably most liable to change while clay-textured soils take much longer.

The effects of environmental changes over time on soil formation are extremely difficult to study, and any conclusions must be treated with considerable caution.

7 Some practical exercises

7.1 Introduction

Although theoretical discussions can be enlightening, many basic principles can be grasped better by investigating soils in the field and in the laboratory. The series of simple exercises below require only rudimentary equipment, but can yield much valuable information. The morphology of soils and their relationship with the environment is best observed in the field, while details of any specific characteristic usually have to be investigated in the laboratory. Nearly all these exercises are suited to either individual or group study.

7.2 Practical work in the field

7.2.1 Site description

A study of soil in the field should always include a description of site conditions and specify the location of the site. *Fig 7.1* shows one possible layout of a site sheet. It is convenient to produce it on one side of A4 paper with enough room for the profile description on the reverse side. Very explicit instructions for field description are to be found in *Soil Taxonomy* [US Soil Survey Staff (1975)] or the *Field Handbook of the Soil Survey of England and Wales* [Hodgson (1974)]. (1974)].

There are examples of sites described conventionally in Chapter Six. However, in some of these descriptions some of the site information has unavoidably been omitted.

Reference
If there are a large number of profiles to be observed they should be given a reference number for easy identification, for example SY1 (= Symons Copse Pit 1). Include the name of the observer so that any problems arising in later analysis can be referred directly to the person who made the initial description.

1 Layer Depth cm	2 Profile Sketch	3 Colour	4 Description of horizons (texture, structure, stoniness, mottling etc.)	5 Field pH value

Samples for laboratory tests taken at:—

1.	cm		5.	cm
2.	cm		6.	cm
3.	cm		7.	cm
4.	cm		8.	cm

Profile description sheet on reverse

Reference No.:   Date:

Grid Ref.:   General Group:

Location: Series:

Elevation (m.):   Described by:

Slope(°):

Topographic Position or
Landform Unit:

Aspect:

Microrelief:

Drainage: Site:
               Profile:

Parent Material:

Vegetation or land use:

Weather:

Climatic data: Rainfall:
                   Temperature:

Other remarks:

Fig 7.1   A site description sheet

Map reference
A six-figure grid reference, together with the topographic map sheet number
and name, should be recorded if possible.

Elevation
This is most easily obtained directly from the map. Alternatively the elevation
above some local datum can be used.

Slope angle
A clinometer gives accurate enough results. Visual assessments are notoriously
inaccurate.

Topographic position
Record the position of the site on the slope, e.g. interfluve, lower concave.
Taken with the slope angles, this may help to explain both the nature of the
parent material and the hydrological conditions prevailing in the profile (*Fig
7.2*). Alternatively, a landscape unit system like the one described by Dalrymple
et al. (1968) can be used.

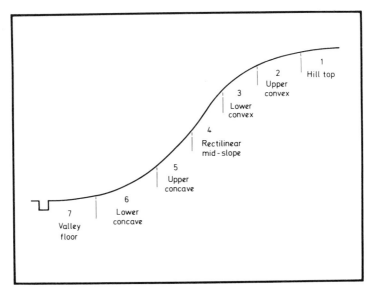

Fig 7.2   A slope unit system

Aspect
This should be given as points of the compass or degrees compass bearing.
Insolation clearly depends on aspect, so the latter may affect, or have affected in
the past, moisture content and soil movement on opposing slopes.

Micro-relief
This can have important effects on the site drainage and consequently on profile morphology. It is important, therefore, to appreciate the detail of relief around the site, e.g. rock outcrops or the ridge and furrow oscillations of the surface (*Fig 7.3*).

Fig 7.3   The micro-relief associated with ridge and furrow, Leicestershire

Site drainage
Loss of soil constituents laterally is closely related to the volume of water passing through the site—in other words, to the site drainage conditions. Sites are commonly referred to as:

- shedding: water drains away rapidly, as on most convex slopes and the upper slopes of hills
- normal: input and output of water are roughly balanced
- receiving: the lateral input of water from upslope in the short term exceeds output
- flooding: subject to periodic inundation by river or sea water

Parent material
We can establish the characteristics of the parent material in several ways:

- by reference to a geological map
- by reference to a soil survey map
- by observing the material *in situ*

Reference to a medium-scale, e.g. 1:50 000, geological map (if available) should determine the age, and possibly the lithology of the solid rock and even any superficial mantle. However, such maps are often not a reliable or sufficiently precise guide to the lithology of the parent material itself. It is evident from several of the examples in Chapter Six that this may be only a thin veneer of a quite different deposit over the mapped material. For example, the geological map might suggest that the bedrock comprised grits of Silurian age, while field observation, indicated that the parent material was a shaley scree overlying the grit. Alternatively, a thin veneer of loess may mantle the solid rock and perform the function of parent material. It is helpful to know how the material originated if it is of a derived nature, e.g.

- till, a poorly sorted material
- solifluction material of angular fragments, often displaying a preferred downslope orientation
- fluvial gravels consisting of well-rounded and sorted pebbles

Climate
Local climate can be surprisingly varied, and elements such as the effective precipitation are important in pedogenic processes. If possible, reliable data should be obtained from a nearby climatological station.

Vegetation
In Chapter Three we dealt at length with the relationship between soil and vegetation. It is obviously essential to study the composition of the vegetation cover. Wherever possible botanical names should be used, since the use of common names often leads to confusion and ambiguities. The species present should be listed, and the relative frequency of each should be indicated. It is useful and convenient to describe the vegetation by reference to the three principal strata:

- the tree layer
- the shrub layer
- the herb layer

Land use
Since land use is likely to affect the nature of the soil-forming processes, present land use and any information relating to past land use should be recorded. The latter is often the only explanation for apparent anomalies in the soil profile.

7.2.2   Profile examination

Equipment
   spade
   trowel
   polythene sheet
   soil colour comparison charts
   soil testing kit
   hand lens
   polythene bags and labels (for sample
      collection, e.g. sandwich bags on a roll)

The essential virtue of a field study is that one can relate the soil to its environment. In some cases this is a complex relationship while in others it may be quite evident. Several points should be borne in mind when selecting a site for investigation. For demonstration purposes a site where a simple profile is likely to be encountered is preferable. It is thus desirable to avoid a site that has been under arable cultivation or is on a steep slope—agricultural practices tend to obscure horizonation in the upper parts of the profile while steep slopes induce colluvial movements which can result in extremely complex soil profiles. A site in a wood, on heathland, or on permanent pasture clearly has much to commend it.

The soil pit
Profiles are best observed in newly exposed road cuttings or in soil pits. When a pit has to be constructed:

- the profile should be clearly revealed and well illuminated, preferably with no shadows on the face to be examined
- there must be easy access for sampling the lower horizons

For group study, a pit of 1 m side is a good size, although for individual work a 50 cm pit may be big enough, but the deeper it is, the larger the ground area will have to be in order to allow excavation and observation. If possible, at least 20 cm of parent material should be exposed.

When digging the pit, remember that the excavated material will have to be replaced as tidily as possible afterwards. This is very important as it will maintain goodwill between pedologist and landowner and enable the site to be visited on further occasions. The turf should be removed carefully and put upside down to one side of the pit. If a sheet of polythene is laid down the soil can be put in a pile on the sheet a little upslope from the pit.

During the excavation the sides of the pits inevitably become smeared. To rectify this a builder's trowel can be used to clean up the face and to reveal the soil structure. Contamination is avoided if one works downwards.

A soil profile is likely to vary considerably from the modal type. In the field, soils frequently do not reveal as clear a pattern as in the illustrations. This should be appreciated when examining soils *in situ* and an accurate description of the profile morphology is obviously vital. Only then can we infer the nature of the pedogenic processes and suggest the environmental controls to which they can be attributed. A convenient way of recording soil properties is by using the field sheet (*Fig 7.1*). A sketch (approximately to scale) can be inserted in column 2 and this enables the position of the horizon boundaries to be recognised at a glance.

Some properties of a soil profile will be more apparent than others, and it is sensible to consider these first.

Colour

If the soil processes have produced any changes, one of the most striking is likely to be a colour change. Since colour is a reflection of other fundamental chemical changes it is useful to record it first. If possible a colour chart such as the Munsell Color Chart or the Revised Soil Color Chart [Oyama and Takehara (1967)] should be employed. Using such a system colours can be compared in terms of hue, chroma and value and designated in a standard form. In the Munsell system the position of any colour in the spectrum is indicated by its hue. Thus 2.5Y is in the yellow zone while 10R is in the red. The value, the second element in the complete designation, refers to its lightness, while the chroma notation indicates its strength, i.e. departure from a neutral of the same lightness. A complete colour description would then be '5YR 5/4 reddish-brown'. Munsell colour designations can be inserted in column 3 of the field sheet. Since moisture content clearly affects soil colour, it is sensible to indicate whether the observation relates to a moist or dry soil.

Horizon depths

The thickness of each horizon should be measured and recorded in column 1. It is convenient to relate depths to a datum at the junction of the mineral and the purely organic horizons. When there is a mull humus the zero is taken as the surface of the soil.

The lines drawn on the diagram may suggest that horizon boundaries are sharp, although we have seen that many process changes are gradual and produce a merging junction. This can usefully be indicated by a dotted line. If the boundary is irregular, this can be represented by a wavy line.

Soil structure

Each horizon should be examined and the structure compared with those in *Fig 2.13*. Often the structure is more clearly revealed after the soil face has dried out. It may be profitable, therefore, to leave this examination until as late as possible if the structure is only weakly revealed. To examine the peds in detail individuals may be picked out with the point of the trowel.

Texture

During the digging of the pit a first impression of the texture will have been gained, but a better impression is obtained by working a small sample between the fingers. The soil needs to be fairly moist in order to assess texture properly, so, if necessary, it should be moistened.

When rubbing the soil between the fingers, a grittiness may be detected which is due to the presence of sand. Silt, on the other hand, produces a slippery or soapy sensation, while any stickiness is caused by clay. The clay content can also be assessed by the ease with which the soil will roll into a 'sausage' shape. Texture determination in the field is thus a matter of balancing the feel of sand, silt and clay.

Where colour differences in the profile are not clear, or where there is a thick horizon, more than one texture assessment should be made for each horizon. Textural differences may form the basis of horizon separation when colour variations are not clear.

Organic matter

In uncultivated soils the nature of the organic accumulation and the extent to which organic material has been translocated are closely dependent on pedogenic processes (Chapter Four). Two aspects of soil organic matter should be investigated:

- the nature of the surface organic horizons
- the location of any translocated organic material

In § 3.2 it was shown that there are basically three types of surface organic matter (*Fig 3.2*):

- mull
- moder
- mor

If the organic material is almost completely incorporated with the mineral matter it can be described as mull. On the other hand, if the organic material exists as separate litter, fermenting and humifying layers which rest on the mineral material we have mor. A partial, but loose, incorporation of the decaying organic matter is found with moder but recognisable H and F horizons can also be identified. The thickness of individual layers should be recorded, starting at the datum of contact between the organo-mineral and the purely organic horizons.

It is quite easy to measure the depth to which organic matter is present in the soil profile. If a small amount of hydrogen peroxide is poured down the soil face most organic matter will react with it, resulting in effervescence through the production of carbon dioxide. The depth to which effervescence extends can be noted.

pH

Many soil processes, as we have seen, are only effective under certain conditions of acidity. The usual measure of acidity, pH, is the negative logarithm of the hydrogen ion concentration of the soil water and is expressed over a range from 0 to 14. pH 7 represents neutrality, while below this is acid and above is alkaline. The simplest, but least accurate, method of determining the pH is with a universal soil indicator such as that supplied by British Drug Houses Ltd. About 2–3 cm of soil is put into a test tube together with an equal amount of barium sulphate. After making a 1:1 soil/distilled water suspension, the indicator is added and the tube shaken thoroughly. The barium sulphate encourages the flocculation of the clay particles, which then sink, leaving a clear supernatant. To permit this the tube must be allowed to stand for a few minutes. The colour of the supernatant can then easily be compared with the standard colour chart supplied, providing an approximate indication of the pH value of the soil to the nearest 0.5 pH unit. The method is fairly fast and simple and is suitable for use in the field. Further samples can be treated while earlier ones are being allowed to stand and clear. Alternatively, a portable electrochemical pH meter can be employed, although this is a delicate instrument and not, in our opinion, well suited to field conditions.

Free carbonates (principally CaCO₃)

Free carbonates (principally $CaCO_3$)

If carbonates are present treatment of the soil with dilute hydrochloric acid (HCl) will liberate carbon dioxide (CO_2), producing an obvious effervescence. A rough assessment of the proportion of carbonates can be made by reference to Table 7.1. The distribution of free carbonates in the profile should be recorded in the comments column of the field sheet.

Cutans, concretions and other deposits

Although much less evident than most of the characteristics so far discussed, secondary accumulations are often symptomatic of particular processes. For instance, the identification of cutans is central in recognising lessivage. Careful and probing observation is, therefore, essential. Any secondary deposits, such as may be caused by incomplete leaching or eluviation, will usually be in the lower parts of the profile. Wherever they are found they may be as pore infillings or as nodules or even as distinct bands and their presence should be noted, with an indication of their composition. Accumulations of carbonates (both of calcium and magnesium) will have been revealed by the previous test, although care should be taken to differentiate between weathered parent material and secondary accumulations. Sodium salts have a characteristic taste and are likely to be reflected in halomorphic vegetation.

Table 7.1   Response of carbonate-rich soils to dilute hydrochloric acid

% CaCO$_3$	Audible effects	Visible effects
0.1	None	None
0.5	Faintly audible increasing to slightly	None
1.0	Slightly audible increasing to moderate	Slight effervescence confined to individual grains; just visible
2.0	Moderate to distinct, heard away from ear	Slightly more general effervescence visible at close inspection
5.0	Easily audible	Moderate effervescence; bubbles to 3 mm; easily visible
10.0	Easily audible	Generally strong effervescence; ubiquitous bubbles to 7 mm; easily visible

[source: Clarke (1971) p. 84]

In temperate climates on acid parent materials (e.g. sandstones, flint gravels), especially those experiencing a high effective precipitation, secondary deposits are likely to be of humus or iron resulting from podzolisation. They can normally be identified by colour: secondary colloidal humus is invariably black and greasy to the touch (on occasion it may be confused with manganese, but normally manganese appears as thin films on ped faces and is often associated with horizons where drainage is impeded); in contrast to these dark deposits the hydrated oxides of iron appear as bright orange or red.

Where lessivage is the dominant process, accumulations of translocated clays are to be expected. In an extreme case clay movement may be revealed by textural differences between the upper and lower parts of the profile. However, as we have seen in § 4.3.3, this is not necessarily due to clay translocation, and closer examination is called for. The clay accumulations are to be expected in the Bt horizons, occurring as cutans lining the major voids between the aggregates. It is useful to have a hand lens (x 10) at this stage since close examination of the peds is necessary in order to identify cutans. A shiny surface is suggestive of clay translocation, whereas a dull face to the ped indicates that weathering *in situ* is the only process operating. These characteristics would aid in distinguishing, for example, a leached brown soil (Udalf) from an acid brown soil (Ochrept) (§ 6.3), the one subject to lessivage and cutan formation, the other formed by intensive weathering and consequently showing a random arrangement of clays which give a dull appearance to the peds.

Collection of samples
None of these observations require any specialised laboratory equipment.

However, it may be necessary to carry out further analysis or one may care to keep a visual record of the soils investigated. In either case samples will need to be collected:

● when it is not vital to preserve the structure, samples for analysis can be collected in polythene bags. About 500 gm per horizon (which can easily be contained in a bag) will be enough for all the laboratory tests described below. If the moisture content is to be determined, the bag should be sealed with adhesive tape or a wire tie. Label the bag using a waterproof fibre-tip pen with the site reference number, horizon and date of collection. Alternatively a label may be tied to the neck of the bag

● where the structure of the soil is to be preserved, the samples should be obtained with the minimum of disturbance and then sealed and labelled as above

To avoid subsequent difficulties, it is vital to record the location and reference number of each sample on the field sheet.

7.3   Practical work in the laboratory

Although the basic morphology of a soil profile, and the relationships between the soil, the parent material and other controlling factors, are best appreciated in the field, much useful information can only be obtained in the laboratory. The procedures set out below have been designed to meet two main requirements. In the first place they are either simple techniques for displaying profile characteristics in convenient form or experiments to establish the type of soil-forming processes at work in the soil. Secondly, only procedures which can be carried out with the most basic equipment have been included. More sophisticated techniques are outside the scope of this book, but those interested in pursuing this aspect further should consult Jackson (1958), Black (1965) or Avery and Bascomb (1974) who include a list of specialist suppliers.

7.3.1   Adhesive tape profiles

This is a simple technique but one which gives a good visual impression of the profile. It is valuable for display purposes but the structure of the soil is not preserved.

Equipment

pestle and mortar
sieves: 210 and 300 μm; receiver
2 microscope slides or stiff card

adhesive tape
white card (for mounting)

Method

Spread out about 50 g of soil from each horizon and leave to air dry. Break up the aggregates using a pestle and mortar. Place the ground sample on a 300 μm sieve stacked over a 210 μm sieve. Fit the lid and receiver and shake for a few minutes. Discard all but the soil collected on the 210 μm sieve.

   To ensure that the tape profile will not exceed 30 cm or so, select an appropriate scaling factor. Place a 40 cm strip of adhesive tape (e.g. Sellotape, Scotch tape) on the bench with the adhesive surface uppermost; turn the ends over to stick to the bench. Next to the tape place a strip of paper showing a scaled-down profile sketch. Use the two microscope slides or pieces of card and place one edge of each across the tape so that they delimit the length required for the first horizon (*Fig 7.4*). Pour the sieved material from this horizon over the tape until the area between the slides is covered. Now press the soil on to the tape and then carefully brush away the surplus. After moving the slides to positions appropriate to the next horizon, repeat the procedure.

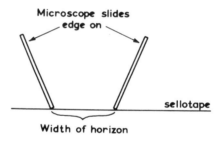

Fig 7.4   The use of microscope slides in adhesive tape profile construction

   The final product will be a scale profile which clearly shows the colour variations. By annotating the profile with structural, textural, pH and other information a clear picture of the soil can be produced. For protection the tape should be mounted adhesive side downwards. Natural profiles can be mounted next to profiles of ignited material for comparison. In this way the colour variations caused by either reduction or organic staining are immediately apparent. Profiles of this type are eminently suitable for inclusion in projects or reports.

   Three-dimensional profiles can be produced using special collecting trays but require much time and effort, both during collection and in preparation for display [see Clarke (1962)].

7.3.2   Determination of field moisture content

Equipment
  oven (capable of heating to 110 °C)
  evaporating basin or tin
  balance (accurate to 0.01 g)

Method
Take the sample from the sealed bag and place it in a weighed dish or tin. Record the total weight and hence calculate the weight of soil, including moisture. Now dry the soil in an oven at 105 °C (220 °F) for at least 16 hours, or, if an oven is not available, air dry for several days. (It should be realised that this does not remove all the moisture, especially from clay soils). Reweigh the dish and contents and from this calculate the dry weight of the soil.

The moisture content on a weight basis is then given by:

$$\frac{\text{weight of moist soil—weight of oven-dry soil}}{\text{weight of oven-dry soil}} \times 100\%$$

7.3.3   Loss on ignition

An approximate determination of organic content

If a sample is heated to *c.* 900 °C several components of the soil are radically altered:

- organic matter is lost by oxidation
- carbonates break down and CO_2 is liberated
- water is driven from the structure of the clay minerals
- ferrous compounds are oxidised to the ferric state

If the sample is heated to *c.* 375 °C only the organic fraction and the ferrous compounds will be affected, although, to ensure total oxidation of these, ignition must continue for at least 16 hours [Ball (1964)]. The loss of weight incurred in this treatment can, therefore, be used to estimate the organic content of the soil.

Equipment
  muffle furnace or bunsen, tripod and pipe-clay triangle
  desiccator
  crucible

Method
Weigh out approximately 20 g of oven-dried soil. Place in a crucible in a muffle
furnace at 375 °C for 16 hours. Remove from the furnace and place in a
desiccator to cool. Weigh and calculate the percentage lost on ignition. In the
absence of a muffle furnace a still more approximate determination can be
made by heating the sample to dull red heat in a crucible over a bunsen burner.
However, it must be appreciated that combined water will be lost from the clays
and CO_2 will be lost from any carbonates present.

  Apart from calculating the loss on ignition, the ignited sample can also be
used to prepare an adhesive tape profile (see experiment 7.3.1). Since all the
ferrous compounds will have been oxidised, and the organic staining removed,
iron which may not have been clear in the field will now be readily apparent as
a rusty hue. For this purpose, ignition over a bunsen is quite satisfactory.

7.3.4   Treatment of a sample containing organic matter

Removal of organic matter from a sample can serve three purposes:

- as a pretreatment before the precise determination of soil texture
- to enable an assessment to be made of the colouration of the soil by organic
  matter
- to illustrate the role played by organic matter in maintaining soil structure

Oxidation of organic matter is most readily accomplished using hydrogen
peroxide which releases carbon dioxide and water.

Equipment
    750 ml conical flask
    sieves: 70, 210, 300, 590 and 2 380 μm; receiver
    wash bottle
    bunsen burner, tripod and gauze
    oven (capable of heating to 110 °C)
    evaporating basins
    6% (20 volume) hydrogen peroxide

Method
Weigh an oven-dried sample of soil to obtain the total weight of mineral and
organic matter (say 50 g). Place this in a conical flask and add 6% H_2O_2 (20
volume) until the soil is covered. Heat very gently (even modest heating will
often cause the sample to boil over). Add more H_2O_2 as required until no
effervescence is observed. In a soil with high organic content this may take some
time. Now transfer the residue into a nest of sieves (2 380 μm, 590 μm, 300 μm,
210 μm, 70 μm, receiver) and wash *gently* until the sample is separated into its

fractions. Separate the sieves and oven dry the material retained on each one. Weigh the aggregates in each size fraction. The loss of weight during treatment can be equated approximately with the weight of organic matter. Finally, express the weight of each size fraction as a percentage of the total weight of mineral matter in the soil.

To determine the effect of organic matter as a bonding agent, take a second soil sample of about the same size as the first. Treat in exactly the same way, but substitute distilled water for the H_2O_2. Dry the fractions retained on the sieves and express the results as percentages as before. By presenting the results side by side comparison can easily be made between treated and untreated samples. In general it will be seen that a much greater proportion of the smaller aggregates is found in the sample treated with hydrogen peroxide. This is mainly due to the removal of the organic bonding agents which hold the aggregates together.

The various size fractions can now be amalgamated. Using a low-power microscope, compare the colour of the mineral grains after treatment with H_2O_2 with that of the untreated grains. It will be seen that organic matter produces a dark staining which is mainly associated with the clay/silt fraction.

7.3.5 Determination of the particle size distribution of a soil sample
[based on British Standard 1377 (1975)]

This experiment conveniently follows on from experiment 7.3.4. The sole objective of the treatment is to ensure the breakdown of all aggregates into the discrete particles of sand, silt and clay. Only when this has been achieved is it possible to establish the relative frequency of these three fractions.

Equipment and reagents
   Whatman no. 50 filter paper
   Buchner filter funnel
   Buchner flask
   filter pump
   stirrer ('milk-shake' type)
   sieves: 70, 210, 300, 590, 2 380μm; receiver
   1 000 ml measuring cylinder
   soil hydrometer (Bouyoucos model)
   dilute HCl (for calcareous soils)
   litmus paper
   sodium hexametaphosphate (Calgon) solution
      (40 g to 1 litre distilled water)

Method
If the sample has been sieved after treatment with H_2O_2 the fractions should be

amalgamated and about 50 ml water added to produce a suspension. If the suspension has a pH greater than 7, 100 ml of dilute hydrochloric acid must be added to remove any free carbonates. (Otherwise proceed to the addition of sodium hexametaphosphate.) Leave the suspension to stand for one hour when it can be filtered under suction through a Whatman no. 50 paper and then wash with warm distilled water until the filtrate shows no acid reaction to litmus. If the soil shows a pH of less than 7, this stage can be omitted.

Finally, 100 ml of sodium hexametaphosphate should be added and the suspension warmed for 10 minutes. By this treatment the polyvalent ions which encourage aggregation are replaced by sodium ions, thereby dispersing the soil. This is especially important since, if silt and clay remain flocculated, they will behave as larger particles during the sedimentation phase of the experiment.

After agitating the mixture for 15 minutes in a 'milk-shake' stirrer (using distilled water), wash the material from the stirrer cup into the nest of sieves.

Dry, resieve and weigh the fractions retained on the sieves. Transfer the mixture that collects in the receiver into a 1000 ml measuring cylinder and top up to 1 litre with distilled water.

In order to determine the proportions of the finer fractions present in the sample, it is necessary to allow the suspension to settle under gravity. Since, according to Stokes' Law, particles settle at a rate which is inversely proportional to the square of their radii, it is possible to separate the coarser from the finer fractions. As material settles out so the specific gravity of the suspension will decrease. By using a soil hydrometer and relying on Stokes' Law, we can calculate the proportions of the various fractions present in the sample.

Before sedimentation, place a rubber bung in the end of the measuring cylinder and shake the cylinder vigorously, thoroughly mixing the contents. Stand the cylinder on a bench and at the same time start a stopclock. After 1 minute place the hydrometer carefully in the suspension and take a reading at 1 minutes 12 seconds. Withdraw the hydrometer slowly and reinsert so that readings can also be made 4 minutes 48 seconds, 2 hours and 8 hours after the commencement of sedimentation.

To calculate the particle size distribution the following relation should be used:

$$K = \frac{R_h}{W_b}\left(\frac{\sigma_s}{\sigma_s - 1}\right) \times 100$$

where K = % material less than a given effective particle diameter
σ_s = specific gravity of solid matter (usually taken to be 2.65)
R_h the hydrometer reading
W_b = oven dry weight of sample after the removal of organic matter

The effective diameters equivalent to the specified settling times, assuming a specific gravity of 2.65, are:

Time	*Effective diameter (mm)*
1 minute 12 seconds	0.04
4 minutes 48 seconds	0.02
2 hours	0.004
8 hours	0.002

The normal way of representing the data from sieving and sedimentation is to plot them on a cumulative graph as shown in *Fig 7.5*.

If the data obtained in experiment 7.3.4 are plotted on the same paper, the effect of complete dispersion by the replacement of divalent cations and by mechanical agitation can be seen. In the specimen treated only with H_2O_2, much of the silt and clay remains aggregated. Thus a higher proportion of 'sand size' material is normally recorded compared with the sample which was completely dispersed.

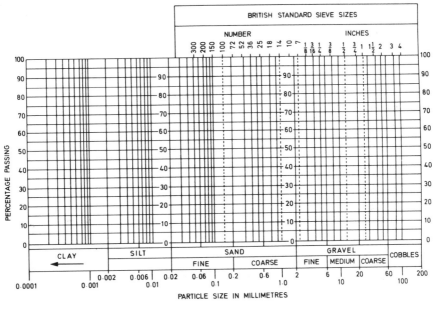

Fig 7.5   Graph for the representation of particle size distributions

7.3.6   Determination of free carbonates

If there are free carbonates, either as $CaCO_3$ or $MgCO_3$, in the soil, they will react with dilute hydrochloric acid to produce CO_2. Various forms of apparatus—for example, the Collins' Calcimeter, the Chittick apparatus—are available which collect and measure the volume of CO_2 generated. Most of these variants are designed to collect the gas at known conditions of temperature and pressure. Once the volume of CO_2 produced is known, the percentage of carbonate in the original sample can be calculated. As the exact nature of the apparatus is liable to vary with manufacture it will not be described in detail here. Determination requires no sample pretreatment other than oven drying and takes 5–10 minutes per determination.

7.3.7   Determination of total extractable iron by colorimetric method*
[after Deb (1949)]

Much of our understanding of soil-forming processes is clearly dependent on a knowledge of the movement of the oxides of iron. One method of extracting these oxides is to react with sodium dithionite, $Na_2S_2O_4$. However, it must be pointed out that this extractant removes all forms of iron oxide and does not enable us to differentiate between, for instance, iron linked with organic compounds and free crystalline iron oxides.

Equipment and reagents
  oven (capable of heating to 110 °C)
  sieve: 2 380 μm
  centrifuge (fitted with 50 ml tubes)
  flask shaker
  water bath (to be maintained at 40 °C)
  measuring cylinder (100 ml)
  pipette (5 ml)
  colour comparator (fitted with Fe disc for
     thioglycollic acid (mercapto-acetic acid) extraction)
  sodium dithionite ($Na_2S_2O_4$)
  hydrochloric acid (0.02N)
  citric acid solution (20% w/w)
  mercapto-acetic acid (thioglycollic acid)
  ammonia solution (10% w/w)
  litmus paper (red)

Method
Remove organic matter by using hydrogen peroxide as described in experiment 7.3.4. Oven dry overnight and weigh out a sample of approximately 1 g of material that has passed through a 2 380 μm mesh sieve. Place the sample in a 50 ml centrifuge tube and make up with 50 ml of distilled water. Shake

* This experiment involves the use of rather more sophisticated equipment than is called for in the other experiments.

thoroughly for three hours to disperse the clay fraction. In order to dissolve the iron, add 2.0 g of sodium dithionite ($Na_2S_2O_4$) and place the suspension in a water bath for 30-50 minutes at 40 °C. Stir the suspension intermittently until the sample is completely bleached. Centrifuge and collect the solution in order to estimate the iron content. Treat the soil residue with a little 0.02N hydrochloric acid to remove any ferrous sulphide and shake thoroughly for 10–15 minutes. Centrifuge again and add the liquid to the existing solution. Accurately measure the volume of the extract (V ml), e.g. by using a graduated pipette.

In a fume cupboard pipette about 1 ml (v ml) of solution into a tube designed for the colour comparator. The volume of extract used will vary according to the amount of iron present and will only be determined by trial and error. Add 0.5 ml of 20% w/w citric acid solution and 1 drop of thioglycollic (mercapto-acetic) acid. Mix well and add enough 10% w/w ammonia solution (usually less than 1 ml) to render the mixture distinctly alkaline (test by litmus). Dilute to exactly 10 ml with distilled water. Place this solution in one of the comparator tubes and place in the comparator (*Fig 7.6*). In the other compartment place a test tube containing a reference blank solution of 0.5 ml citric acid, 1 drop of thioglycollic acid and the same volume of ammonia solution as used in the extract. Add distilled water to 10 ml.

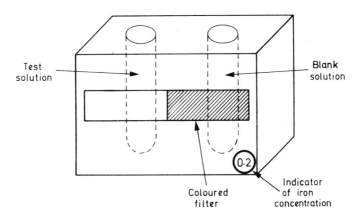

Fig 7.6   The colour comparator

Hold the comparator before a uniform source of white light (e.g. a north window) and compare the colour produced in the test solution with the colours in the standard disc until a colour match is obtained. The weight of soluble iron, w (in mg) contained in the test solution is indicated in the comparator window.

Conventionally, the proportion of iron present is expressed as % Fe_2O_3 in the original oven-dry sample:

$$\%Fe_2O_3 \text{ in oven-dry sample} = \frac{w}{1000} \cdot \frac{V}{v} \cdot \frac{160}{112} \cdot \frac{100}{\text{O.D. wt of sample}}$$

where $\dfrac{160}{112}$ is $\dfrac{\text{molecular wt of } Fe_2O_3}{2 \times \text{atomic wt of Fe}}$

and w = weight of iron in test solution (mg)
     V = total volume of extract (ml)
     v = volume of extract used in determination (ml)

7.3.8   Analysis of the microfabric of the soil

Equipment
   sheet of plate glass
   Canada Balsam sticks
   xylene
   microscope slides
   hotplate
   junior hacksaw and blades
   carborundum powders (coarse, medium and fine grades)
   liquid paraffin
   microscope

The shape of individual mineral particles and their relationship to one another is best seen by examining a very thin slice of soil (thin section) under the microscope. Voids and secondary accumulations such as cutans and nodules are also seen well by this technique. It should be borne in mind that preparation is somewhat lengthy and demands care. However, it yields valuable results which are especially useful for demonstration purposes.
   A basic requirement is a piece of plate glass of at least 30 cm diameter on which the sections can be ground.

Method
Immerse a small block of dried soil of size, say, 3 cm in xylene to remove air. Allow to stand for a few minutes. This, and other operations before grinding, should take place in a fume cupboard or, at the very least, a well-ventilated room. Melt some Canada Balsam in a small tin on a hotplate. As soon as it is molten, place the soil block in it directly from the xylene. Place a thick microscope slide on the hotplate to warm. Rub a solid stick of Canada Balsam on the slide until it is covered with a thin molten film. Transfer the impregnated block of soil to the slide, taking care to avoid trapping air bubbles. Remove from the hotplate and allow to cool. When the preparation has set hard, cut the impregnated block with a fine hacksaw or a diamond wheel leaving a thickness of about 2 mm of soil on the slide. Finish on the glass plate using coarse and then fine grinding

paste (carborundum powder and liquid paraffin). As the section is ground to near its finished state, care must be taken to produce a section of uniform thickness—and one must also be careful not to destroy it completely. When ready for viewing it should be less than 25µm and clearly translucent. There is no need to use a cover slip and the slide can be viewed directly. (*Fig 7.7*). The grinding process should take about 30 minutes.

Fig 7.7   A soil thin section mounted on a microscope slide and the impregnated soil block from which the sample was obtained. On the right is the finished slide

7.3.9   The hydrological properties of the soil

Many soil processes and responses depend directly and indirectly on the way in which water passes through a soil. Furthermore, in any assessment of land potential it is important to know as much as possible about the drainage and water retention properties of the soil. Water can move either in spaces between individual mineral grains (textural pore space) or between the aggregates (structural pore space). The latter pores, being relatively large, form the principal route for water movement under saturated conditions (for instance, after a heavy storm), but as the soil becomes unsaturated, movement is confined to the smaller pores which are generally those within the peds. Naturally, any fine material moving in suspension tends to travel via the larger voids. Evidence of this is seen in the form of clay skins which tend to mantle the peds in the Bt horizon of leached brown soils (Udalfs). Through these major interpedal voids air also enters the soil.

Clearly a well-connected structural void system is the most effective in ensuring free drainage. If vertical connections are poor, restricted drainage and aeration are likely to promote gleying. Again, the larger the structural units, the lower the density of interstructural voids and usually the slower the drainage. If, therefore, we can obtain an idea of the relative proportions of the smaller and larger pores, this will provide an approximate indication of the drainage properties of the soil. Fairly large samples will be needed in an investigation into the hydrological properties of the soil, since only in this way will adequate representation of the structural voids be achieved. Two experiments which can be carried out using basic equipment and which provide valuable information on soil hydrology are:

- the determination of the moisture characteristic curve
- the determination of the saturated hydraulic conductivity

The moisture characteristic (pF) curve
Before considering how this curve is constructed, we must explain the forces which retain water in pores. In its simplest form a pore may be considered as a capillary tube into which water will penetrate and be retained by the forces of surface tension (*Fig 7.8*). To withdraw the water from such a pore requires the application of suction or pressure. If suction is applied to a specimen of soil, the larger pores will drain almost at once, but water will only be removed from the finest voids on the application of pressure of several atmospheres. By plotting a curve of applied suction against moisture content an accurate indication of the pore size distribution will be obtained.

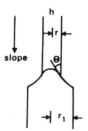

Fig 7.8   Soil tension forces in a capillary-sized soil pore. Water is isolated in a soil pore of radius r, the weight of the water column ($\pi r^2 \rho g$) being supported by a surface tension force (τ) at the water-pore wall boundary ($2\pi r \tau \cos\theta$) Pore r_1 has drained because the weight of the water has exceeded the surface tension force

It is mainly the larger pores which conduct water, as many of the very small pores are not interconnected, and moisture conductivity via water films in these small pores is very low. Thus a soil which retains much moisture in its pores at high suctions is likely to have poor conducting properties and is often characterised by gleyed horizons.

Equipment

alloy or rigid plastic tube (5 cm inside diameter)
wooden rod (5 cm diameter)
non-ferrous metal or rigid plastic tube (as above)
  cut to lengths of 2–3 cm
fine cutting wire (such as is used for cheese)
No 4 grade immersion filter (sintered glass)
  6 cm diameter
2 metres of PVC tubing (inside diameter to provide a
  tight fit over the sintered glass immersion filter)
retort stand, clamps
metric rule
spatula
oven (for sample drying)
No 42 grade filter paper

Method

To obtain large undisturbed samples, push an alloy or plastic tube of at least 5 cm diameter and 15 cm length into the ground and carefully dig it out. Extrude the soil into tubes of exactly the same diameter but of 2–3 cm length using a wooden rod (*Fig 7.9*). Carefully cut the soil flush at both ends of these smaller tubes with a wire. Several samples prepared in this way will indicate the range of variability of moisture characteristics even within soils which appear to be of similar morphology.

Place the prepared sample on a no. 42 grade filter paper and stand in distilled water to saturate. This should be complete in twenty-four hours.

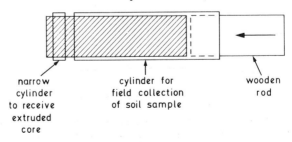

narrow
cylinder
to receive
extruded
core

cylinder for
field collection
of soil sample

wooden
rod

Fig 7.9   Extruding a soil sample using a wooden rod

Assemble the tension plate apparatus shown in *Fig 7.10* using about two metres of PVC tubing connected to a sintered glass immersion filter (grade 4) of 6 cm diameter (or bigger if samples of larger diameter are used). Boil a quantity of distilled water for 30 minutes to remove dissolved air. Fill the immersion filter and tubing with this de-aired water and mount the apparatus on a retort stand. Make sure that no air enters the system. Place the soil sample and filter paper on the immersion filter. The soil pores are now connected to the water manometer via the water-filled pores in the immersion filter. Raise the manometer to bring water on to the surface of the filter and then lower the free end a few centimetres and allow the system to stabilise overnight. Equilibrium is achieved when the meniscus reaches a steady position, which may take several hours. The applied suction (S cm water) can be taken as the difference in height between the meniscus and the centre of the sample. When equilibrium has been attained remove the sample with a spatula and weigh; then replace it on the filter. Lower the free end of the tube and again allow to attain equilibrium. After the last desaturation stage has been completed weigh it and then oven dry.

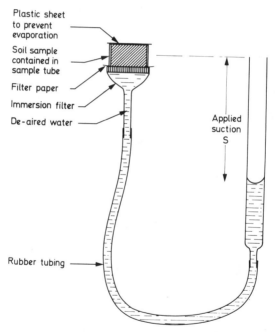

Fig 7.10   The tension plate apparatus for obtaining soil moisture characteristic curves

The moisture content equivalent to each applied suction can be calculated as described in experiment 7.3.2. Finally plot moisture content against applied suction (*Fig 7.11*). The suction value is normally expressed as a logarithm to base 10—referred to as soil pF. By expressing the suction in this way a wide range of suction values can be shown on one graph. Changes of suction near to saturation are more significant for water conduction than changes at low moisture contents. By employing a log scale the 'wet end of the curve' can be given suitable emphasis.

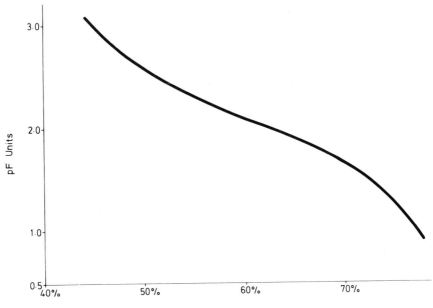

Fig 7.11   A soil moisture characteristic (pF) curve

Determination of saturated hydraulic conductivity
While it is possible to determine the hydraulic conductivity of a soil at any moisture content, the techniques required for other than saturated conductivity are difficult and will not be discussed here. It is generally true that field methods of measuring conductivity are preferable to laboratory determinations, largely because of disturbance incurred during sampling. However, it is frequently more practical to make comparative determinations in the laboratory.
Determinations of two types are possible:

● on an undisturbed sample
● on a dried and sieved sample

A reconstituted sample is easy to prepare but its conductivity will be quite different from that of a natural soil. However, it is useful if the objective is to demonstrate conductivity differences between soils of differing textures.

Equipment
  funnel
  measuring cylinder
  stopclock

Method
Obtain undisturbed samples as in the previous experiment and place one of these in water on a filter paper with the water close to the top of the tube. Allow the sample to saturate for at least 24 hours before removing. Attach an empty cylinder to the top of the sample cylinder with a rubber band or with waterproof tape (*Fig 7.12*) so that a water-tight joint is made.

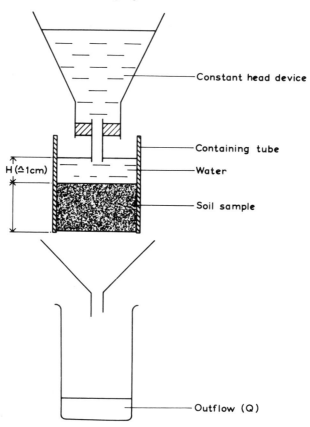

Fig 7.12   Apparatus for the determination of the saturated hydraulic conductivity of a soil sample

To prevent aggregates being lost from the sample, support the two tubes on a fine wire mesh grid. This could be a small diameter 210 µm soil sieve. Arrange a constant head device so that the water in the empty tube is about 1 cm deep and record the outflow into the cylinder over measured periods, usually of at least 15 minutes. Make successive measurements until the outflow tends to a constant value, which may be used in calculating the saturated conductivity.

The saturated hydraulic conductivity of the soil is given by Darcy's Law:

$$\frac{Q}{At} = K \frac{H}{l}$$

Where Q = outflow (ml)
A = area of sample (cm^2)
t = time increment (sec)
K = hydraulic conductivity (cm sec^{-1})
H = head of water (cm)
l = length of sample (cm)

This experiment is easily repeated and illustrates well the variation which occurs in saturated conductivity as weil as in many other soil properties. This variability can be simply expressed in statistical terms, enabling comparisons to be made of the variation displayed by different soils or even different horizons. Gregory (1973) discusses suitable statistical treatments for this type of material.

References

● Ahn, P. (1970)
  West African Soils, OUP, 332 pp
● Andersen, S.T. (1979)
  Brown earth and podzol: soil genesis illuminated by microfossil analysis
  Boreas **8**, 59–73
● Anderson, D.W. (1979)
  Process of humus formation and transformation in soils of the Canadian Great
  Plains
  J. Soil Sci. **30**, 77–84
● Atkinson, H.J. and J.R. Wright (1957)
  Chelation and the vertical movement of soil constituents
  Soil Sci. **84**, 1–11
● Avery, B.W. (1964)
  The Soils and Land Use of the District around Aylesbury and Hemel Hempstead,
  HMSO, 216 pp
● Avery, B.W. (1973)
  Soil classification in the Soil Survey of England and Wales
  J. Soil Sci. **24**, 324–38
● Avery, B.W. & C.L. Bascomb (1974)
  Soil Survey Laboratory Methods
  Soil Survey Tech. Monograph No. 6, Harpenden, 83 pp
● Ball, D. (1964)
  Loss on ignition as an estimate of organic matter and organic carbon in
  non-calcareous soils
  J. Soil Sci. **15**, 84–92
● Bascomb, C.L. & M.G. Jarvis (1976)
  Variability in three areas of the Denchworth soil map unit. 1. Purity of the
  map unit and property variability within it.
  J. Soil Sci. **27**, 420–37

● Bie, S.W. & P.H.T. Beckett (1971)
Quality control in soil survey. Introduction.
J. Soil Sci. **22**, 32–49
● Birkeland, P. (1975)
Pedology, Weathering and Geomorphological Research
OUP, New York, 285 pp
● Birot, P. (1968)
The Cycle of Erosion in Different Climates
Batsford, 144 pp
● Black, C.A. (ed.) (1965)
Methods of Soil Analysis (2 vols)
Amer. Soc. Agron., Madison, Wisconsin, 1572 pp
● Bloomfield, C. (1951)
The mechanism of gley formation
J. Soil Sci. **2**, 196–211
● Bloomfield, C. (1953)
A study of podzolisation I. The mobilisation of iron and aluminium by Scots Pine needles
J. Soil Sci. **4**, 5–16
● Bloomfield, C. (1954)
A study of podzolisation V. The mobilisation of iron and aluminium by aspen and ash leaves
J. Soil Sci. **5,** 50–56
● Bloomfield, C. (1955)
A study of podzolisation VI. The immobilisation of iron and aluminium
J. Soil Sci. **6**, 284–92
● Brewer, R. (1976)
Fabric and Mineral Analysis of Soils
Krieger, Huntington, New York, 482 pp
● Brewer, R. (1968)
Clay illuviation as a factor in particle-size differentiation in soil profiles
Trans. 9th Int.Cong.Soil Sci., Adelaide **4**, 481–88
● Bridges, E.M. (1966)
The soils and land use of the district north of Derby
Mem. Soil Survey Gt. Britain, Harpenden, 112 pp
● British Standards Institution (1975)
Methods of Testing Soils for Civil Engineering Purposes, B.S. 1377: 1975
British Standards Institution, 143 pp
● Broadbent, F.E. (1955)
Basic problems in organic matter transformation
Soil Sci. **79**, 107–14
● Brown, E.H. (1960)
The Relief and Drainage of Wales: a study in geomorphological development

Univ. of Wales Press, Cardiff, 186 pp
- Brown, G. (1953)
  The occurrence of lepidocrocite in some British soils
  J. Soil Sci. **4,** 220–8
- Bruckert, S. & F. Jacquin (1969)
  Complexation du fer (III) par les fractions organiques d'un extract naturel de mor
  C.R. Acad. Sci. Paris D, 2169, 1625–8
- Bunting, B.T. (1967)
  The Geography of Soil 2nd edition
  Hutchinson, 213 pp
- Burges, A. (1967)
  The decomposition of organic matter in the soil
  in *Soil Biology* A. Burges and F. Raw (eds)
  Academic Press, 479–92
- Carroll, D.M., R. Evans and V.C. Bendelow (1977)
  Air photo-interpretation for soil mapping
  Tech. Monog. No. 8
  Soil Survey of England & Wales, Harpenden, 85 pp
- Catt, J.A. (1979)
  Soils and Quaternary geology in Britain
  J. Soil Sci. **30,** 607–42
- Catt, J. *et al.* (1971)
  Loess in the soils of Norfolk
  J. Soil Sci. **22,** 444–52
- Chartres, C. (1980)
  A Quaternary soil sequence in the Kennet Valley, central southern England
  Geoderma **23,** 125–46
- Claridge, G.G.C. & I.B. Campbell (1968)
  Some features of Antarctic soils and their relation to other desert soils
  Trans. 9th Int. Cong.Soil Sci., Adelaide **4,** 541–9
- Clark, F.E. (1967)
  Bacteria in soil
  in *Soil Biology* A. Burges & F. Raw (eds)
  Academic Press, 15–49
- Clarke, G.R. (1962)
  Preparation and preservation of soil monoliths of thin section
  J. Soil Sci. **13,** 18–21
- Clarke, G.R. (1971)
  The Study of Soil in the Field 5th edition
  OUP, 145 pp
- Conacher, A.J. & J.B. Dalrymple (1977)

The nine unit land surface model. An approach to pedogeomorphic research
Geoderma **18**, 1–154
● Coulson, C.B, R.I. Davies & D.A. Lewis (1960)
Polyphenols in plant, humus and soil I. Polyphenols of leaves, litter and superficial humus from mull and mor sites
J. Soil Sci **11**, 29–43
● Crampton, C.B. (1963)
The development and morphology of iron pan podzols in mid and South Wales
J. Soil Sci. **14,** 282–302
● Cruickshank, J.G. (1972)
Soil Geography
David & Charles, Newton Abbot, 256 pp
● Curtis, L.F., F.M. Courtney & S. Trudgill (1976)
Soils in the British Isles
Longman, 364 pp
● Dalrymple, J.B., R. Blong & A. Conacher (1968)
An hypothetical nine unit land surface model
Z. Geomorph. **12**, 60–76
● Deb, B.C. (1949)
The estimation of free iron oxides in soils and clays and their removal
J. Soil Sci. **1**, 212–20
● Dimbleby, G.W. (1963)
The Development of British Heathlands and their Soils
Oxford Forestry Mem. No. 23
Clarendon Press, Oxford
● Dokuchaev, V.V. (1886)
Data on land appraisal in Nizhnii-Novgorod province
in *Collected Works* Vol. 4
Acad. Sci., Moscow, 1950
● Dokuchaev, V.V. (1900)
Pektsie o Pochvovedenie
in *Collected Works* Vol. 7
Acad. Sci., Moscow, 1955
● Dowling, J.W.F. (1966)
The mode of occurrence of laterites in northern Nigeria and their appearance in aerial photography
Eng. Geol. **1**, 221–33
● Duchaufour, P. (1968)
L'Evolution des sols
Masson, Paris, 94 pp
● Duchaufour, P. (1970)

Précis de pédologie 3rd edition
Masson, Paris, 481 pp

● Duchaufour, P. (1976)
Dynamics of organic matter in soils of temperate regions: its action on pedogenesis
Geoderma **15**, 31–40

● Duchaufour, P. & B. Souchier (1978)
Roles of iron and clay in genesis of acid soils under a humid, temperate climate
Geoderma **20**, 15–26

● Edwards, A.P. & J.M. Bremner (1967)
Microaggregates in soils
J. Soil Sci. **18**, 64–73

● Ellis, J.G., D.F. Acton & H.C. Moss (1967)
The Soils of the Willow Bunch Lake Map Area, 72H
Saskatchewan Inst. Pedology, Publication No. S2, Saskatoon, 97 pp

● Evans, L.J. & W.A. Adams (1975)
Quantitative pedological studies on soils derived from Silurian mudstones
V. Redistribution and loss of mobilised constituents
J. Soil Sci. **26**, 327–35

● FAO/UNESCO (1974)
FAO/UNESCO Soil Map of the World; 1:5 million Vol. 1
Legend, Paris

● Federoff, N. (1966)
Contribution à la connaissance de la pédogenèse Quaternaire dans la sud-ouest du bassin parisien
Bull. Ass. fr. Etude du Sol **2**, 94–106

● Fitzpatrick, E.A. (1967)
Soil nomenclature & classification
Geoderma **1**, 91–105

● Fripiat, J.J. (1965)
Surface chemistry and soil science in *Experimental Pedology* (Proc. 11th Easter School in Agricultural Science, Univ Nottingham) (Hallsworth, E.G. & D.V. Crawford, eds)
Butterworth, 3–13

● Gerasimov, I.P. (1974)
The age of recent soils
Geoderma **12**, 17–25

● Gerasimov, I.P. & M.A. Glazovskaya (1965)
Fundamentals of Soil Science & Soil Geography
Israel Prog. Scient. Translations, Jerusalem, 382 pp

● Glentworth, R & H.G. Dion (1949)
The Association or hydrologic sequence in certain soils of the podzolic

zone of north-east Scotland
J. Soil Sci. **1**, 35–49

● Gregory, S. (1973)
Statistical Methods and the Geographer 3rd edition
Longmans, 271 pp

● Grim, R.E. (1968)
Clay Mineralogy 2nd edition
McGraw Hill, 596 pp

● Guillet, B., J. Rouiller & B. Souchier (1975)
Podzolisation and clay migration in spodosols of eastern France
Geoderma **14**, 223–45

● Hall, A.D. & E.J. Russell (1911)
Report on the Agriculture & Soils of Kent, Surrey & Sussex
HMSO, 206 pp

● Hallsworth, E.G. & D.V. Crawford (eds) (1965)
Experimental Pedology
Butterworth, 414 pp

● Handley, W.R.C. (1954)
Mull and Mor Formation in Forest Soils
For. Comm. Bull. No. 23
HMSO, 115 pp

● Hodgson, J.M. (ed) (1974)
Soil Survey Field Handbook
Tech. Monog. No. 5
Soil Survey of England and Wales, Harpenden, 99 pp

● Hubert, P. (1961)
Verklarende tekst bij het Kaartblad Poperinge 81W
Bodemkaart Van Belgie, Gent

● Hunt, C.B. (1972)
Geology of Soils: their evolution, classification and uses
W.H. Freeman & Co.

● International Society of Soil Science (1967)
Proposal for a uniform system of soil horizon designation
Bull.Int.Soc.Soil Sci. **31**, 4–7

● Jackson, M.L. (1958)
Soil Chemical Analysis
Prentice Hall, Englewood Cliffs, 498 pp

● Jarvis, R.A. (1968)
The Soils of the Reading District
Agric.Res.Council, Harpenden, 150 pp

● Jenny, H. (1941)
Factors of Soil Formation: a system of quantitative pedology
McGraw Hill, New York, 281 pp

● John, D.T. (1980)
The soils and superficial deposits on the North Downs of Surrey
in *The Shaping of southern England* D.K.C. Jones (ed.)
Inst. Brit. Geogs. Special Pub. No. 11, 101–30
● Joffe, J.S. (1949)
Pedology
Pedological Publications, New Brunswick, 662 pp
● Kantor, W. & U. Schwertmann (1974)
Mineralogy and genesis of clays in red-black toposequences on basic
igneous rocks in Kenya
J. Soil Sci. **25**, 67–78
● Kellogg, C.E. (1974)
Soil genesis, classification and cartography, 1924–74
Geoderma **12**, 347–62
● Kendrick, W.B. (1959)
The time factor in the decomposition of coniferous leaf litter
Can. J. Bot. **37**, 907–12
● King, L.C. (1962)
Morphology of the Earth
Oliver & Boyd, Edinburgh, 699 pp
● Kononova, M.M. (1966)
Soil Organic Matter 2nd edition
Pergamon, Oxford, 544 pp
● Kubiëna, W.L. (1953)
The Soils of Europe
Murby, 318 pp
● Lévêque, A. (1967)
Les Sols ferrallitiques de Guyane française
Office de la Recherche Scientifique et Technique Outre-mer, Paris, 168 pp
● Loveday, J. (1962)
Plateau deposits of the southern Chiltern Hills
Proc. Geol. Ass. **73**, 83–102
● Loughnan, F.J. (1969)
Chemical Weathering of the Silicate Minerals
Elsevier, Amsterdam, 154 pp
● McGown, A. & P. Iley (1973)
A comparison of data from agricultural soil surveys with engineering
investigations for roadworks in Ayrshire
J. Soil Sci. **24**, 145–56
● Mackney, D. (1961)
A podsol development sequence in oakwoods and heath in central England
J. Soil Sci **12**, 23–40
● Marbut, C.F. (1928)

A scheme of soil classification
Trans. 1st Int.Cong.Soil Sci., Washington **4**, 1–31

● Matthews, J.A. (1980)
Some problems and implications of ^{14}C dates from a podzol buried beneath an end moraine at Haugabreen, southern Norway
Geografiska Annaler **62A**, 185–208

● Milne, G. (1935)
Composite units for the mapping of complex soil assocations
Trans. 3rd Int.Cong.Soil Sci., Oxford **1**, 345–7

● Milne, G. (1947)
A soil reconnaissance journey through parts of Tanganyika Territory, Dec. 1935 to February 1936
J. Ecology **35,** 192–265

● Mitchell, B.D. & R.A. Jarvis (1956)
The Soils of the Country round Kilmarnock
HMSO, Edinburgh, 234 pp

● Mitchell, C.W. (1973)
Terrain Evaluation
Longmans, 221 pp

● Mitchell, C.W. (1975)
The applications of LANDSAT 1 imagery to the Sudan Savanna Project
J. Brit. Interplanetary Soc. **28**, 659–72

● Mohr, E.C.J., F.A. van Baren & J. van Schuylenborgh (1972)
Tropical Soils 3rd edition
Mouton, The Hague, 481 pp

● Moore, P.D. & D.J. Bellamy (1972)
Peatlands
Elek, 221 pp

● Mortland, M.M. (1970)
Clay-organic complexes and interactions
Adv. Agron. **22**, 75–117

● Nye, P.H. (1954)
Some soil forming processes in the humid tropics. Part 1
J. Soil Sci. **5**, 7–27

● Nye, P.H. (1955)
Some soil forming processes in the humid tropics. Part 2
J. Soil Sci. **6**, 51–62

● Oertel, A.C. (1968)
Some observations incompatible with clay illuviation
Trans. 9th Int.Cong.Soil Sci., Adelaide **4**, 481–8

● Ollier, C.D. (1969)
Weathering
Oliver & Boyd, Edinburgh, 304 pp

- Oyama, M. & H. Takehara (1967)
  Revised Soil Color Charts
  Fujihara Industry Co Ltd, Tokyo
- Pidgeon, J.D. (1976)
  Contemporary pedogenetic processes in a ferrallitic soil in Uganda. I. Identification
  Geoderma **15**, 425–36
- Pizer, N.H. (1931)
  A Survey of the Soils of Berkshire
  Univ. Reading, Fac.Agric. Hort.Bull. 39
  Reading, 141 pp
- Ponomareva, V.V. (1969)
  Theory of Podzolisation
  Israel Prog.Scient.Translations, Jerusalem, 309 pp
- Proudfoot, V.B. (1958)
  Problems of soil history. Podzol development at Goodland and Torr townlands, Co. Antrim, N. Ireland
  J. Soil Sci. **9**, 186–98
- Rudeforth, C.C. (1970)
  Soils of North Cardiganshire
  Agric.Res.Council, Harpenden, 153 pp
- Russell, E.W. (1971)
  Soil Structure: its maintenance and improvement
  J. Soil Sci **22**, 137–51
- Russell, E.W. (1973)
  Soil Conditions and Plant Growth, 10th edition
  Longmans, 849 pp
- Schnitzer, M. & S.I.M. Skinner (1963)
  Organo-metallic interactions in soil. I. Reactions between a number of metal ions and the organic matter of a podzol Bh horizon
  Soil Sci **96**, 86–93
- Schuffelen, A.C. (1974)
  A few aspects of 50 years of soil chemistry
  Geoderma **12**, 281–97
- Schuylenborg, J. van (1971)
  Weathering and soil-forming processes
  in *Soils and Tropical Weathering*
  UNESCO, Paris, 39–50
- Segalen, P. (1971)
  Metallic oxides and hydroxides in soils of the warm and humid areas of the world: formation, identification, evolution
  in *Soils and Tropical Weathering*
  UNESCO, Paris, 25–38

- Sibertsev, N.M. (1899)
  Pochvovedenie
  in *Selected Writings* Vol. 1
  Acad. Sci., Moscow, 1951
- Smyth, A.J. & R.F. Montgomery (1962)
  Soils and Land Use in Central Western Nigeria
  Govt of Western Nigeria, Ibadan, 265 pp
- Sturdy, R.G., R.H. Allen, P. Bullock, J.A. Catt & S. Greenfield (1979)
  Paleosols developed on chalky boulder clay in Essex
  J. Soil. Sci. **30,** 117–37
- Tedrow, J.C.F., J.V. Drew, D.E. Hill & L.A. Douglas (1958)
  Major genetic soils of the Arctic slope of Alaska
  J. Soil Sci. **9**, 33–45
- Tedrow, J.C.F. & L.A. Douglas (1964)
  Soil investigations on Banks Island
  Soil Sci. **98**, 53–65
- Tedrow, J.C.F. & D.E. Hill (1955)
  Arctic brown soil
  Soil Sci. **80**, 265–75
- Thomas, M.F. (1966)
  Some geomorphological implications of deep weathering patterns in crystalline rocks in Nigeria
  Trans.Inst.Br. Geogr. **40**, 173–93
- Thomasson, A.J. (1971)
  Soils of the Melton Mowbray District
  Mem.Soil Survey Gt. Britain, Harpenden, 118 pp
- Townshend, J.R.G. (ed.) (1981)
  Terrain analysis and remote sensing
  Allen and Unwin
- US Soil Survey Staff (1975)
  Soil Taxonomy. A basic system for making and interpreting soil surveys
  Agric. Handbook no. 436
  Soil Conservation Service, US Dept Agric., Washington, 754 pp
- Vine, H. (1949)
  Nigerian soils in relation to parent materials
  in *Proc. of the Commonwealth Conf. on Tropical and Sub-tropical Soils (1948)*
  Commonwealth Bureau of Soil Science Techn. Comm. No. 46, 22–9
- Walker, D (1970)
  Direction and rate in some British post-glacial hydroseres
  in *Studies in the Vegetational History of the British Isles* (Walker, D. & R.G. West, eds)
  CUP, 117–39

● Watson, J.P. (1975)
The composition of termite (Macrotermes spp) mounds on soil derived from basic rock in three rainfall zones of Rhodesia
Geoderma **14**, 147–58
● Weaver, C.E. & L.D. Pollard (1973)
The Chemistry of Clay Minerals
Elsevier, Amsterdam, 213 pp
● Webster, R. (1968)
Fundamental objections to the Seventh Approximation
J. Soil Sci. **19**, 354–66
● Westin, F.C. & C.V. Frazee (1976)
LANDSAT data, its use in a soil survey program
Soil Sci. Soc. Amer.Proc. **40**, 81–9
● White, L.P. (1977)
Aerial photography and remote sensing for soil survey
Clarendon Press, Oxford, 104 pp
● Wilson, K. (1960)
The time factor in the development of dune soils at South Haven peninsula, Dorset
J. Ecol. 341–59
● Wintle, A. (1981)
Thermoluminescence dating of Late Devensian loess in southern England
Nature **289**, 479–80
● Wooldridge, S.W. & D.L. Linton (1955)
Structure, Surface and Drainage in South-east England 2nd edition
Philip, 176 pp
● Worster, D. (1979)
Dust Bowl
OUP, New York, 277 pp
● Young, A (1976)
Tropical Soils and Soil Survey
CUP, 468 pp

Further reading

This is a list of some of the more widely available texts which are most useful for student reference. They were published in London, unless otherwise stated.

● Battey, M. (1972)
Mineralogy for Students
Longman, 323 pp
● Birkeland, P.W. (1974)
Pedology, Weathering and Geomorphological Research
OUP, 285 pp
● Brady, N.C. (1974)
The Nature and Properties of Soils 8th edition
The Macmillan Co., New York, 639 pp
● Bridges, E.M. (1978)
World Soils 2nd edition
CUP, Cambridge, 128 pp
● Cruickshank, J.G. (1972)
Soil Geography
David & Charles, Newton Abbot, 256 pp
● Curtis, L.F., F.M. Courtney & S. Trudgill (1976)
Soils in the British Isles
Longman, 364 pp
● Fitzpatrick, E.A. (1971)
Pedology
Oliver & Boyd, Edinburgh, 306 pp
● Gray, T.R.G. & S.T. Williams (1975)
Soil Micro-organisms
Longman, 240 pp
● Goudie, A. (1973)
Duricrusts in Tropical and Sub-Tropical Landscapes
Clarendon Press, Oxford, 174 pp

● Hallsworth, E.G. & D.V. Crawford (eds) (1965)
  Experimental Pedology
  Butterworth, 414 pp
● Mitchell, C.W. (1973)
  Terrain Evaluation
  Longman, 221 pp
● Ollier, C. (1969)
  Weathering
  Oliver & Boyd, Edinburgh, 304 pp
● Pears, N. (1977)
  Basic Biogeography
  Longman, 272 pp
● Russell, E.W. (1973)
  Soil Conditions and Plant Growth 10th edition
  Longman, 849 pp
● Seddon, B. (1971)
  Introduction to Biogeography
  Duckworth, 220 pp
● Simpson, B. (1966)
  Rocks and Minerals
  Pergamon, Oxford, 302 pp
● Wells, A.F. (1962)
  Structural Inorganic Chemistry, 3rd edition
  OUP, 1055 pp

In addition, the wide range of memoirs published to accompany the maps of the Soil Survey of Scotland (HMSO, Edinburgh) and the Soil Survey of England and Wales (Rothamsted Experimental Station, Harpenden, Herts) are invaluable sources of reference for British soils.

Index

Definitions of terms are in italics; principal references are in bold type.

accommodation, *degree of particle or ped packing*, 32, Fig. 2.12
acid brown soils, **113,** 123, 174; *see also* cambic horizon
acidification, **67,** 71, 157
acidity, 26; measurement, 173
Actinomycetes, **46,** 55
active layer, *see* seasonally thawed layer
aeolian (wind blown) material, 31
aerial photographs, 98, 101
aerobic conditions, organic decomposition in, 44
aggregates, *see* peds
aggregate strength, 35; in acid environments, 60; in calcareous environments, 60
aggregation, 35; biotic activity and, 35, 45; fragmentation and, 35
agricultural revolution, 2
agric horizon, 92
albic horizon, 92, 112
algae, 48
alumina, octahedron, 17, Fig. 2.6
aluminium: cause of acidity, 26; hydrous oxide, 63, 68
aluminosilicates, 17, Table 2.1
ammonification, 55
amphiboles, 18, Table 2.1
Amulet association, 139ff.
anaerobic conditions, *being deficient in oxygen*: organic decomposition in, 44, **55,** 118; effect on gleying, 74

Aquents, 133, 151, Table 5.4
Aquepts, 105, 120, 130, Table 5.4
Aquods, **113,** 122, Table 5.4
Aquolls, 140, Table 5.4
arctic brown soils, 107, Fig. 6.6
arctic meadows, 106, Fig. 6.4
Ardill association, 31, Table 2.4
argillic horizon, *a B horizon containing illuviated clay*, 69, 92; *see also* B-textural horizon, cutans
Aridisols, 136, Table 5.4
Arthropods, 44, 48
aromatic ring structures, 49
ashen (Ea) horizon, 72, 112; *see also* albic horizon
Association, soil, 101, **103,** 118, Fig. 6.14
augite, *silicate of Ca, Al, Fe or Mg*, 18, Table 2.1
Aylesbury area, England, 126ff.
azonal soils, 87, Table 5.1

B-textural horizon, 68, 113, 145; *see also* argillic horizon
bacteria, *see* micro-organisms
basement rocks, as parent material, 144
basin peat, 76, 118
Batcombe series, 127
bicarbonate, production, 66
bioclimatic zones, 87
biosystem, relation with soils, 6
biotite, $K(Mg, Fe)_3 (Al, Si_3O_{10}) (OH)_2$, *a sheet silicate*, 17, Table 2.7
blanket bog, 76, 118
blocky structure, 34, 35
bog soils, 107

bonding agents, *see* cements, flocculation
Borolls, 135, 139ff., Table 5.4
breakdown of peds, 68
Bridgnorth series (acid brown soil), 29, Table 2.4
brown calcareous soils, 66, 109, **113,** 130
brown earths, 113, Fig. 6.9; *see also* acid brown soils, leached brown soils
brown humic acids, **50,** 55, 56
brunizems, 135
Bunter sandstone, as parent material, 29, Table 2.4
burial mounds, 159

calcareous parent materials, 60, 113
calcic horizon, 92
calcification, 66
cambic horizon (Bw), *a horizon due to weathering,* **61,** 92, 113
Canadian Arctic, 105
carbohydrates, 41, 48, Table 3.3
carbonates, 56, 63, 66, 139, **173,** Table 7.1; determination of, 181
carbonation, 19
carbon dioxide (CO_2), 19, 20
carbon-nitrogen ratio (C/N), **56**
carboxylic acids, 71
catena, 143, Fig. 6.28
cations, *ions having a positive charge,* 18; effect on flocculation, 35, 63; recycling, 67
cation exchange, **26,** 67
cation exchange capacity (C.E.C.), *the total potential of a soil for adsorbing cations,* 24, Table 2.2, Table 3.2; of organic matter, 41, Table 2.2, Table 3.2
cation hydration, 24, Fig. 2.8
cements, between soil particles, 36
cellulose, *an easily decomposed carbohydrate,* 41, 51, 55, Table 3.3
chalcedony ($nSiO_2$), Table 2.1
chalk, as parent material, 126, 129, Fig. 6.10
chalk head, 60, 126, 130
chelation, *solution of metals by organic compounds,* 72
chemical weathering, 18ff.
chernozems, 52, 135, Figs 6.23, 6.24
chert ($nSiO_2$), Table 2.1
chestnut soils, 135, 138, 139, Fig. 6.24
citric acid, 71, 73

classification, 85ff.
clastic sediments, 15, 29
clay, *a particle of less than* 2μm, 29; as a parent material, 130
clay minerals, *secondary aluminosilicate minerals having a sheet structure and a high charge to volume ratio,* 20ff., 28, 62; effect on aggregation, 35; mode of formation, 22
clay skins, *see* cutans
Clay-with-Flints, 126, 129
climate, relation with, 7, 157
coatings, *see* cutans
colloid, *particle* <1μm, 28
colour, *see* soil colour
compound structure, Table 2.5
concretions, 173; *see also* iron concretions
coniferous forest, soils of, 70, **110,** 159
Coombe series, 130
covalent bonding, *the sharing of electrons by adjacent atoms to form a molecule,* in minerals, 15
crumb structure, Table 2.5
cryoturbation, 103, Fig. 6.2
cuirasse, *see* duricrust
cutans, *accumulations coating grains or lining the walls of soil pores,* **69,** 149, 161, 173

decalcification, 139, 157
deciduous woodland, impact on production of organic acids, 67; soils of, 110ff.
deflocculation, clay, 68
diffuse electrical double layer, 25
dispersing agents, 180
dispersion, clay, 67
Dokuchaev, 3, 86, 87
drumlin landscape, soils in, 120
duricrust, *a caprock usually of ironstone, in sub-humid tropical regions,* 81, **152,** 154, Figs 4.11, 4.12, 6.33

earthworms, 44, 48, 61, 111, **147,** Fig. 6.32
efflorescences, 64
electrostatic forces, 23, 24, 35
eluviation, *the physical movement of material in suspension,* 63
England and Wales, Soil Survey of, classification of, 94, Table 5.6
Entisols, 153

equatorial climate, 78
erosion, 6, 142, Fig. 1.3
eutrophic (*nutrient rich*) peat, 77
Evesham series, 29, Table 2.4

factorial equation, 6
fats, 41
feldspars, *K, Na, Ca (Al,Si3O8) framework silicates*, 17, Table 2.1
fen peat, 118
fermentation layer (F), 44, Fig. 3.2
ferrallitisation, 78ff., 153ff.
ferrallitic soils, 154, 155, Table 6.1, Fig. 4.10
ferric oxide, 36
ferromagnesian minerals, *aluminosilicates containing a high proportion of iron and magnesium and usually readily susceptible to weathering*, 62; *see also* mafic minerals
ferrous-organic complex, 72, 74
ferruginous crust, *see* duricrust
ferruginous soils, *see* tropical ferruginous soils
fertility, 2, 27
field work, 165ff.
flint (nSiO2), Table 2.1
flint gravels as parent material, 131
flocculation, *aggregation of clay and humus colloidal particles into domains by electrostatic forces*, 35, Fig. 2.15; in calcareous environments, 60; in acid environments, 60
forest, supply of organic debris, 43
forest mull, 61
fragipan, *a very dense horizon of low porosity which is brittle on drying*, Table 1.1
freeze/thaw, *see* frost shattering
frost heave, 105
frost shattering, 13, Fig. 2.2, Fig. 2.3
fulvic acids, 50, 55, 56, 68, 71
fungi, 44, **48**, 53, 55

geographic associations, soil, 103
geomorphology, relation of soils with, 6
gibbsite, Al(OH)3 (alumina), **23**, 79, 153, Table 2.1
gleyed podzol, 113
gleyed tundra soil, 105
gleying process, 73ff..
gley soils, 105, 116, 123, 124, 140, 141, 151, 156

goethite, αFeO(OH), **23**, 62, 74, 79, **153,** Table 2.1
granular structure, Table 2.5
grassland: supply of organic debris from, 43, 115; soil development under, 135ff.
grey humic acids, **50**, 55, 56
ground water gley, 74, **116**, 133, 151, Fig. 6.12
gums, *see* polysaccharides
gypsic horizon, 92

heathland, effect on soil formation, 70, 110
hematite, Fe2O3, 23, 62, Table 2.1
hemicellulose, 41
hill creep soils, 145
hill peat, 118, 122
hill wash soils, 146
Hiraethog series, 101, 124
Histosols, 107, 118
horizons, 2, 7, Table 1.1; *see also* soil horizons
hornblende, *hydroxyl bearing mafic mineral*, Table 2.1
humic acids, 41, 50; *see also* grey humic acids
humic layer (H), 44, Fig. 3.2
humification, *the production of insoluble colloidal organic materials*, 55ff.
humod, 112
humus, 48ff., Table 3.2
humus iron podzol, 72, 112, 131
hydration, 20
hydraulic conductivity, determination of, 189, Fig. 7.12
hydrogen ion, 18
hydrogen bonding, **24**, 38, Fig. 2.8
hydrology, influence of site, **116**, 123, 139
hydrolysis, 18
hydromorphic soils, *subject to regular waterlogging*, 74
hydrous micas, *a family of 2:1 lattice clay minerals*, 21, Fig. 2.7
hydrous oxides, e.g. gibbsite, goethite, **23**, 36, 78, Fig. 2.16; mobilisation, 70, 71; immobilisation, 72

Icknield series, 129
illite, *see* hydrous micas
inorganic chemical weathering, 18ff.
intrazonal soils, 87
involutions, 105, Fig. 6.2

iron, role in aggregate stability, 60
iron concretions, formation of: in gleys, 72ff.; in ferruginous soils, **150,** 154, 156
iron oxides, 23, 62, 63; determination of, 182
iron pans, formation of, 112
iron podzol, 112
ironstone crust, *see* duricrust
isomorphous substitution, 21
Iwo association, 145ff., Fig. 6.29

joints, role in weathering, 13

kaolinite, *a family of 1:1 lattice clay minerals,* **21,** 79, 149, Fig. 2.7
Kilmarnock area, 118ff., Fig. 6.15
Kilmarnock series, 101, 120
Kilmaurs series, 101, **121**
krotovina, 66
Kubiena, classification, 89, Table 5.3

laminar structure, 34, Fig. 2.13, Fig. 2.14
Landsat imagery, 97, Fig. 5.1
landscape units, 167
laterisation, *see* ferrallitisation
laterite, *see* plinthite, duricrust
latosolisation, *see* ferrallitisation
leached brown soils, 113, 126, 127, 128, 133
leaching, *the movement of materials in solution,* 63
lepidocrocite, $\gamma FeO(OH)$, 74, Table 2.1
lessivage, 67ff., 141, Fig. 4.4, Fig. 4.5
Lias shales, Table 2.4; as parent material, 29
lichen, 48, Fig. 2.4
lignin, *carbohydrate relatively resistant to biochemical decomposition,* 41ff., 51ff., 77, Table 3.4
limonite, $\alpha FeO(OH)$, *sometimes used to describe amorphous ferric oxides,* 23, 62, Table 2.1
lithosols, 152
litter layer (L), 44, Fig. 3.2
loess: as parent material, 113, 138, 161; effect on texture, 31, Table 2.4
loss-on-ignition, determination of, 177

mafic minerals, ferromagnesian minerals, 17, Table 2.1
Manod series, 101, 124

mapping, 97ff.
Marbut classification, 85, 89, Table 5.2
massive structure, 34, Table 2.5
master horizons, 8, Table 1.1
mechanical composition, 27ff.
micas, *sheet silicates,* 17, Table 2.1; *see also* hydrous micas
microfabric analysis, 184
micro-organisms, *bacteria, Actinomycetes, fungi and algae,* 44, **46,** 47, 52, 53, 55, 67, Fig. 3.3, Fig. 3.12
minerals, *see* primary minerals, clay minerals
mineralisation, *breakdown of organic matter into largely soluble and gaseous compounds,* 51ff.
mites, 44, 48, Fig. 3.3
moder, 45, 172, Fig. 3.2
moisture content, determination of, 177
moisture characteristic curve (pF), 186ff., Fig. 7.11
mollic horizons, 135
Mollisols, 52, 134ff.
montmorillonite, *family of 2:1 lattice clay minerals which allow the ingress of water molecules,* 21, 156, Fig. 2.7
mor, **45,** 56, 70, 159, 172, Fig. 3.2
mottled zone: associated with ferrallitisation, 79, 149; in gleyed soils, 73, 116, Fig. 6.12, Plate 6
mull, 45, 55, 60, 115, 172, Fig. 3.2
muscovite, *white mica KAl_2 (Al, Si_3O_{10}) $(OH)_2$,* 17, Table 2.1

natric horizon, 92
nitrates, 53, Fig. 3.6
nitrites, 53, Fig. 3.6
nitrogen containing compounds (proteins and amino-acids), 41, 50, 55, Table 3.1
nitrogen cycle, 53, Fig. 3.6
nutrients, 27

Ochrepts, 66, 109, **120,** 123, 124, 130, 174
oligotrophic (*nutrient deficient*) peat, 77
olivine *$(Mg, Fe)_2SiO_4$*, Table 2.1
Orders, soil, 90, Table 5.4
organic chemical weathering, 20ff.
organic colloids, 36, **48ff.,** Table 2.2
organic matter: bonding agent, 38; decomposition, 48ff.; nature, 41ff., 49; origin and incorporation, 43ff.;

removal, 178
organic soil, *see* peat
organisms, 46ff.
Orthids, 107
orthoclase, 17, Table 2.1
Orthods, 72, 112, 113, 131
ortstein, 112
overgrazing, 141
oxalic acid, 71, 73
oxic horizon, 92
oxidation, 19

parent material, *the little-weathered fragmented bedrock or transported sediment*, 3, 168
particle size distribution, determination of, 179
patterned ground, 109, Fig. 6.7
peat: characteristic vegetation, 77, Fig. 3.7; formation, 44, 76ff., 106; micro-organism levels, 76
peaty podzols, 113, 122, Fig. 6.17
pedalfers, *soils without free calcium in the profile*, 85, **89**
pedocals, *soils with free calcium in the profile*, 85, **89**
pedogenic factors, 6, **59**; *see also* biosystem, parent material, toposequence, time
pedon, *smallest three dimensional soil unit which can represent the nature and arrangement of horizons*, 9, Fig. 1.5
peds, *natural soil aggregates*, 3, **31,** 56
permafrost, 103
pF curve, *see* moisture characteristic curve
pH, *negative logarithm of the hydrogen ion concentration*, 26; *see also* acidity
physical weathering, 12ff.
placic horizon, 93
plagioclase, 17, Table 2.1
plant roots, as weathering agents, 14
Plateau Drift, 126, Fig. 6.19
platy structure, 34, Fig. 2.13, Fig. 2.14
plinthite, *tropical soil horizon heavily indurated with sesquioxides*, 81, 152
Plynlimon area, Wales, 122ff., Fig. 6.18
podzolic brown earth, 112, 113
podzolisation, 70ff., 83, 110, 112, 159
podzols, 110ff., Figs. 4.6, 6.8
polar desert soils, 107

polymerisation, 49, 55
polyphenols, **49,** 53, 55, 68, 72, Fig. 3.4
polysaccharides, 38, 41, **53,** 56, 60, 64, Table 3.4
prairie, 134ff.
prairie soils, 135, Fig. 6.24
primary minerals, *formed during vulcanism, metamorphism, or as a precipitate in sediments*, 15ff.
prismatic structure, 34
profile examination, 170
protein, 41, 48, 50, 53, Table 3.1, Table 3.4
pyroxenes, Table 2.1

quartz ($nSiO_2$), 15, Table 2.1
quinones, 49, Fig. 3.4

rain forest, soil development under, 135ff.
Reading area, 131
red colour, *see* rubefication
redox potential, 80
regosols, 142
Rendolls, 52, **113,** 129, Fig. 6.11
rendzina, 52, **113,** 129, Fig. 6.11
resins, 41
ridge and furrow, 168, Fig. 7.3
river terraces, soil development on, 131
rubefication, *in situ weathering and reorganisation of ferric oxides in hot and seasonally moist climates resulting in the production of a deep red colour*, 61, **62,** 79, 145, Fig. 4.1

St Albans series, 133
salic horizon, 93
saline soils, 64
salinisation, 64
salts, mobility of, 64
sample collection, 174
sand, *a particle of between 2mm and 20μm diameter*, 27, Table 2.3
sand dunes, soil development in, 157
Saskatchewan area, 138
satellite imagery, 97, Fig. 5.1
savanna, soil development under, 143ff.
seasonally thawed layer, 103
secondary minerals, 20ff.
sedentary soils, 146
sedimentation and soil formation, 157, **161**

Series, soil, *soils with similar profile characteristics developed on lithologically similar parent materials*, 85, 89, 101
sesquioxides, *the oxides and hydroxides of ferric iron and aluminium, see* hydrous oxides
Seventh Approximation, 85, **89,** Table 5.4
shrinkage of clays, 22
shifting cultivation, 2
Sibertzev, classification, 85, Table 5.1
sierozems, 136
silica, mobilisation, 71, 78
silica tetrahedron, 15, Fig. 2.5
silt, *a particle of between 2 and 60 μm diameter*, 28, Table 2.3
simple structures, Table 2.5
site description, 165, Fig. 7.1
slope movement, and soil formation, 103, 113, **122ff.,** 143, **145**
smectite, *see* montmorillonite
sodium cation, effects of domination on colloids, 35
soil: defined, 4, 11, Fig. 1.2; boundaries, 99; classification, 86ff.; colour, 4, 171, Fig. 4.1; complex, *a mapping unit which includes soils of more than one taxon*, 101; horizon, *a soil layer having sensibly uniform characteristics*, 2ff., horizon nomenclature, 8, 44, Table 1.1; mapping, 97ff.; organisms, 46ff.; pedon, 9, Fig. 1.5; porosity, 3; profile, 4; reaction, 26, 173; structure, 3, 31ff., 171, Table 2.5, Fig. 2.13; texture, *an expression of the proportion of discrete sand, silt and clay particles*, 2, 27ff., 172, Fig. 2.10; classification systems, 27, Table 2.3; water, 24ff.
solifluction, 103, 129
solonchak, 142, Fig. 4.3
sols bruns acides, *see* acid brown soils, 109
sols bruns lessivés, *see* leached brown soils, 113
solum (pl. sola), *A, E and B horizons*, 3, Fig. 1.2
solution, 20, Fig. 4.9
Southampton series, 131
South Haven peninsula, 157, Fig. 6.36
spheroidal structure, 34
spodic horizon, 93
Spodosols, 110ff.

springtails, 44
stability of peds, 35
stagnogley, *see* surface water gley
starches, 41
steppe, soils of, 134ff.
strength, ped, *see* aggregate strength
structure, *see* soil structure
Sub-orders, soil, 90, Table 5.4, Table 5.5
sugars, 41
surface area/volume ratio, 12, Fig. 2.1
surface tension (& soil water), 24
surface water gley, 74, 116, 121, 130, Fig. 6.12
surveying, soil, 97ff.
swelling of clays, 22

taxonomy, *see* classification
termites, 147, Fig. 6.31
terrain units, 98
texture, *see* soil texture
Thames series, 133
till, as a parent material, 31, 60, 110, 123, 138, Table 2.4
time in soil formation, 157ff.
toposequence, *see* Association
translocation, *redistribution of components in the soil*, 63ff., Fig. 4.2
tropical ferruginous soils, 145ff., Fig. 6.30
tubules, 74, Fig. 4.7
tundra soils, 103ff., Fig. 6.1

Udalfs, 113, 127, 128, 133, 135
Udolls, 135
USDA classification, *see* Seventh Approximation
Ustalfs, 145ff.
Ustolls, 135

vegetation, and nutrient cycling, 61, 67
Vertisols, 156, Fig. 6.35

Waals, van der, forces, **38,** 70
water table: influence on gleying, 74; influence on peat, 76
waxes, 41, 48, Table 3.1
weathering, *physical and/or chemical disintegration of rocks and minerals*: 11ff., 59ff., Fig. 2.3; in temperate environments, 60; in tropical climates, 61, **78,** 143
weathering products, 20ff.

Wicken series, 130
Winchester series, 128

Xerolls, 135

Ynys series, a ground water gley, 101,
123, 124

zonal soils, 85, **87**